HOW TO STOP TAKIN

DR PETER TYRER is a
Mapperley Hospital, Notting
Cambridge University (1959-   ыained at St
Thomas's Hospital, London (1962–1965). He had
further training in psychiatry at Maudsley Hospital,
London. He is Assistant Editor of the *British Journal of
Psychiatry*, Member of Council of the British Associ-
ation of Psychopharmacology and a Clinical Teacher at
the University of Nottingham Medical School. He has
been involved in research into common mental dis-
orders since 1969. His previous books are *How to Sleep
Better*, *How to Cope with Stress* (both Sheldon), *The
Role of Bodily Feelings in Anxiety* (OUP) and *Drugs in
Psychiatric Practice* (Butterworths). He has also written
extensively for professional journals. He is married,
with three children.

Overcoming Common Problems Series

Overcoming Common Problems Series

Overcoming Common Problems Series

Overcoming Common Problems

HOW TO STOP TAKING TRANQUILLISERS

Dr Peter Tyrer
MD, MRCP, FRCPsych.

SHELDON PRESS
LONDON

First published in Great Britain in 1986 by
Sheldon Press, SPCK, Marylebone Road, London NW1 4DU

All profits from the sale of this book will be spent
on research into tranquilliser dependence.

British Library Cataloguing in Publication Data

Tyrer, Peter
    How to stop taking tranquillisers. —
(Overcoming common problems).
    1. Tranquillizing drugs   2. Medication
abuse — Treatment
    I Title   II. Series
    616.86'3   RC568.T/

    ISBN 0-85969-504-2
    ISBN 0-85969-505-0 Pbk

Typeset by Deltatype, Ellesmere Port
Printed in Great Britain by
Richard Clay (The Chaucer Press) Ltd,
Bungay, Suffolk

To Beryl and Brian, who first showed me that
tranquilliser dependence could be beaten

Contents

Acknowledgements

I should like to thank Heather Ashton, Jane Bristow, Anne Gell, Cosmo Hallstrom, Malcolm Lader, Siobhan Murphy, Robert Owen, Shirley Trickett, and Stephen Tyrer for stimulating discussions that have led to the writing of this book

1

Tranquilliser Dependence –
The Facts

It is now difficult to talk about taking tranquillizers without the problem of dependence being mentioned. Many of those who are taking tranquillisers believe themselves to be addicted, and many more who could benefit from taking them are afraid to do so in case they become addicted. Yet 15 years ago people were quite happy to take these drugs and, apart from some concern about the barbiturates, problems of dependence were seldom raised. It was even suggested that most tranquillisers were so safe that it was not necessary for doctors alone to prescribe them; social workers, district nurses and health visitors should be able to provide them too, as their work often involved seeing people who needed calming down.

What has changed in the past fifteen years? Why are people now so concerned about tranquilliser dependence? Why did it take so long for this potential problem to be discovered? If these drugs cause addiction why are they ever prescribed? I shall be dealing with all of these questions in the following pages but, first, we need to know something about the effects of tranquillisers on the mind and body and be clear what is meant by the terms dependence and addiction.

What are tranquillisers?

As the name suggests, these drugs create calm and tranquillity and, in larger doses, bring on sleep. They are used for calming people when they feel unduly anxious or nervous and for helping those who have insomnia. They act mainly on the brain but because this is such a complicated organ they have many other effects apart from sedation.

Almost all tranquillisers reduce the activity of brain cells and are technically called cerebral depressants for this reason. This surprises many people who experience stimulant effects after taking these drugs. For example, when you take the oldest known tranquilliser, alcohol, you often get a feeling of increased confidence and alertness. If you drink too much, this effect passes quickly but in small amounts alcohol does seem to be a stimulant, although this is not really the case. Tranquillisers also remove many of the inhibiting effects of the brain but, here too, the apparent stimulating effect is misleading. The drug merely peels away the inhibitions that prevent us from acting as we really are, not necessarily as we should like the world to see us. The removal of these inhibitions leads to a feeling of release that is often stimulating.

Two groups of tranquillisers are used most commonly today.

- The first group slows down all parts of the brain and for this reason such tranquillisers are often called general central depressant drugs. Barbiturates, alcohol and a drug called chloral are the main members of this group. Chloral is the safest of the three and barbiturates the most dangerous, although alcohol is close behind.

  In small amounts they merely remove inhibitions. When given in larger quantities they affect your judgement so that you tend to act irresponsibly. In still larger amounts they make you feel sleepy. When an overdose is taken, sleep becomes so deep that there may be no response to any form of stimulation. This is the state of coma and is close to death. Eventually, the parts of the brain concerned with keeping us alive are also depressed by the drug and stop working. The heart fails, the lungs cease to function and the patient can only be kept alive on a life support machine.

- The second group of drugs is more specific – that is, they act on the parts of the brain that are concerned with making us more or less anxious. These drugs have much less effect on other functions, so they are much safer than alcohol and the barbiturates. Almost all the drugs in this group are benzodiazepines. This word is quite a mouthful, but it describes a basic chemical structure possessed by all drugs in the group. Valium is the best known of the benzodiazepines but others are mentioned later in this book.

2

The reason why benzodiazepines pick out anxiety and nervousness while largely ignoring other parts of brain function is that they act on special sites in the brain, called benzodiazepine receptors. These only allow benzodiazepine drugs, or very similar substances, to attach to them. Once the drugs become attached to the receptors the nerve pathways are stimulated and anxiety is reduced.

Drugs that do not attach themselves to benzodiazepine receptors cannot work in this way; instead they reduce anxiety by slowing all parts of the brain's function. An analogy can be made with the ignition key of a car. If the right key is chosen, the ignition is switched on, the engine is started and the car can then be driven off at a good speed with only the driver operating it. If the correct ignition key is not available and it is not known how to short-circuit the ignition, the car can travel at speed only with the help of a large number of people pushing it, a most inefficient means of transport.

The benzodiazepine drugs are the ignition keys for relieving anxiety. They tune in to the body's own engine of anxiety control and their tranquillising effects are more natural than the central depressant drugs.

Other calming drugs

Many other drugs have calming effects but are not officially called tranquillisers. Those that act on the mind are called psychotropic drugs. This group includes antidepressants, drugs for Parkinson's disease, pain killers, and antipsychotic drugs (the antipsychotic drugs are sometimes called major tranquillisers). All these drugs may cause some degree of sedation but this is only a secondary effect that has nothing to do with their main action.

Many people who are nervous about dependence on tranquillisers think that all psychotropic drugs are suspect. This is a mistaken view. For example, the antipsychotic drugs were originally called major tranquillisers simply because they calmed down the agitated behaviour of patients with severe mental illness such as schizophrenia. In low doses they have a mild calming effect in nervous people also. So it is important to realize that major tranquillisers do *not* carry any important risk of dependence.

Most of the other psychotropic drugs also carry little or no risk of dependence. But because many are taken regularly to prevent recurring episodes of mental illness such as depression, it would be unwise to stop them without approval from your doctor beforehand.

What is drug dependence?

Dependence on a drug can be either mental (psychological) or physical.

- Psychological dependence describes the patient's need to go on taking a drug because it is producing pleasurable effects or at least removing unpleasurable ones.
- Physical dependence describes the need of the body to continue receiving a drug whether or not it has any such benefits. This type of dependence is shown mainly by withdrawal symptoms. When the drug has been taken for some time it becomes accepted as a normal part of the body's contents. If it is suddenly withdrawn the body cries out for more and, if none is forthcoming, reacts by producing a host of physical symptoms. These vary for different drugs but they all have some common features, including feelings of agitation and distress, sweating, palpitations, trembling, feeling sick, light-headed or dizzy, dry mouth and hot and cold flushes. These symptoms are accompanied by a craving for the drug. If the drug is given, the symptoms disappear – but they can only be kept at bay by taking the drug regularly.

With many forms of physical dependence the body gets so used to the drug that more and more needs to be taken to produce the desired effects. With hard drugs such as heroin and morphine, life becomes a constant quest to get supplies for the next 'fix'. In technical language, the body becomes 'tolerant' to the drug so that, after regular use, the originally effective dose no longer produces any response.

As you might expect, drugs that do not produce tolerance in the body are usually less dangerous but they can still produce physical dependence. All of us know people who have smoked tobacco for many years. The amount they smoke may vary a little, increasing at times of stress and reducing when things calm down again, but the average amount of tobacco smoked remains much the same over the years. The nicotine in each cigarette has the same effect after 20 years of smoking as after only six months. When such people stop smoking they get at least some of the withdrawal symptoms mentioned earlier, together with cravings for tobacco. These have them panting for a smoke again. After a few deep breaths of tarry smoke laced with nicotine their withdrawal symptoms disappear and they are again at peace with the world.

Tranquilliser dependence is most often like tobacco dependence. People take the same dose of drug for a long period and do not tend to increase it. They may acquire a little tolerance and complain that the drug seems to be losing its effects slightly but they do not need to have the dose increased significantly.

However, with central depressants such as alcohol and barbiturates, tolerance is more of a problem. If increasing doses are taken it can lead to a roller-coaster of growing dependence, more severe withdrawal symptoms and a situation that becomes indistinguishable from dependence on hard drugs.

Most people have heard of the worst form of withdrawal symptoms following alcohol dependence – delirium tremens (D.T.'s for short). The patient suffers from something close to pure terror; in addition to the physical symptoms already mentioned everything round about him carries threat and he experiences bizarre hallucinations. These are frightening shapes and figures of animals or men and they all seem about to attack the patient. This is why he pulls the sheets over his head and screams. The most effective treatment for D.T.'s is the original drug of dependence – alcohol – but both doctor and patient know that this will only solve the problem temporarily.

Tranquilliser dependence, as we shall see later, can be just as unpleasant as delirium tremens, although there are some important differences. Dependence ranges from mild psychological dependence to severe addiction. In its mildest form people feel that they still need to take a small dose of tranquilliser 'to keep well'. It is almost like an insurance policy. The tranquilliser may no longer be doing any good but the person is too nervous to stop it. Incidentally, all pills – including dummy pills or placebos – can produce psychological dependence so it has nothing to do with what is in the pill.

At the other extreme are a few patients who take massive doses of tranquillisers, have severe withdrawal symptoms if they reduce or stop taking their drugs, and will do almost anything to get further supplies.

How common is tranquilliser dependence?

Approximately one in five adults in most countries in the world take a prescribed tranquilliser at some time in their lives. The incidence of taking tranquillisers is nearly trebled if tobacco and alcohol are included. And approximately 5 per cent develop some degree of dependence on their drugs. Put another way, approximately 500,000 in the United Kingdom and five million in Europe and America are, or have been, mildly or severely addicted to tranquillisers. So the problem is a common one.

It is impossible to predict who will develop dependence on tranquillisers. However, we do know most of the factors that increase the risk of dependence.

- The most obvious factor is the length of treatment. Some people fear that after taking one tablet only they may be hooked for life. This is not so. Regular treatment every day for at least two weeks is the minimum period necessary for some dependence to develop but even then it is rare. The risk increases with the length of treatment, up to a period of a year but there is no evidence that physical as opposed to psychological dependence continues to increase significantly thereafter.

    However, the longer a tranquilliser is taken the greater is the likelihood of psychological dependence. The benzodiazepines have been available on prescription for twenty-five years and the barbiturates for at least fifty years so it is possible for patients to have taken tranquillisers regularly for most of their lives. Someone who has taken a drug for twenty-five years will not find it as easy to stop as someone who has only taken it regularly for one year.

- The higher the dose of a tranquilliser the greater the risk of dependence. It used to be thought that only people who took very high doses regularly became dependent. Now it is realized that even in the low doses often used to treat anxiety it is sometimes difficult to stop because of withdrawal symptoms.

When deciding on what is a high or low dose it is important to know the nature of the drug as well as the dose. Many people think that if they take five milligrams of one drug it will have less effect than taking 10 milligrams of another. This may not be the case. To find out the equivalent dose (i.e. the dose that produces the same effect) of each tranquilliser, please refer to the table on page 3.

- People who have had any form of drug dependence in the past are more likely to become dependent on tranquillisers. So if you are a regular cigarette smoker who cannot stop or have had a problem with stopping alcohol in the past you should be cautious about taking tranquillisers, particularly in regular dosage. This may have something to do with personality – whether you are a strong or weak character, a calm or nervous one. If you are the anxious or nervous type, even when there is nothing to worry about you will probably still be anxious and therefore more susceptible. Of course, there are many other types of personality apart from the anxious ones and these are described fully in an earlier book in this series, *How to Cope with Stress* (Sheldon Press).

People who do tend to worry excessively and need the support of others are more likely to become dependent on tranquillisers. Unfortunately, they are also more likely to be treated with them. When these people stop taking tranquillisers they tend to return to their normal worrying selves. Consequently they will get many anxious symptoms and as many of these feelings are the same as those experienced in withdrawal reactions it might be assumed, wrongly, that they are withdrawal symptoms.

These various considerations make interpretation of symptoms after withdrawing tranquillisers a difficult task. And there are others. For instance, we have no means of knowing whether people are dependent on tranquillisers until they start reducing or stop taking their drugs. We also need to have a clear understanding of the withdrawal syndrome before we can decide that an individual *is* dependent on tranquillisers.

The most important thing about a withdrawal syndrome is that it is a temporary situation. Unpleasant feelings (panic, moodiness, palpitations, nausea, hypersensitivity to light and noise) noted after stopping the drug will only last for a short time because they are simply a response to the drug gradually disappearing from the body. After a few days, or at the most a few weeks, the drug will be completely eliminated and all withdrawal symptoms will disappear. If, however, some of these unpleasant feelings persist for many months after withdrawal they can no longer be regarded as real withdrawal symptoms. They could be a return of the symptoms the person experienced before he ever had tranquillisers, but there is another explanation.

Many people cannot cope with the normal stresses of everyday life after stopping tranquillisers, even when the withdrawal symptoms have passed. This may be because the normal ways of coping that all of us have to learn in order to deal with these stresses have to be re-learned after tranquillisers have been stopped – and this can take several months. But these feelings of not being able to cope are usually different from those of physical withdrawal and consist of anxiety and tension.

The important thing to know is how many people who start taking tranquillisers become dependent. Let us consider an average group of 100 people who are prescribed tranquillisers. Almost all of these will be taking their tablets to control anxiety or to help them to sleep but about seven will be taking them for another medical condition. Sixty-eight will take a short course of tranquilliser, lasting only a few weeks, after which time they will reduce and stop their tablets without any major problems. They are likely to have been prescribed their tranquilliser after a major upset, such as the severe illness of a close relative, and when this crisis is past they will no longer need their tablets.

However, about thirty of those who stop taking tranquillisers after a few weeks will have minor difficulties if they stopped taking their tablets suddenly. These difficulties, often described as rebound anxiety, include a temporary return of some of their old symptoms and occasionally some new ones also. This mild form of dependence is much easier to overcome than that created by long-term use.

Of the remaining thirty-two people who take tranquillisers for six weeks or longer, eleven will take the tablets for up to twelve months and then stop without too much difficulty. They will probably not take the tablets regularly throughout this period, relying on them only when they have special difficulty in sleeping or feel more nervous than usual. Consequently, they do not develop dependence and have no problems in stopping when the drugs are no longer needed.

Nine of the 100 will take their tablets regularly for many months and in some cases for a few years. This will include many of the group taking the tranquillisers for medical reasons such as epilepsy as well as an important group taking them for insomnia only. This latter group will not have withdrawal symptoms when they stop taking tranquillisers but will have a return of their original problem because it is a chronic one.

The remaining twelve, including about seven who have nervous or dependent personalities, will develop full tranquilliser dependence. They may take the tablets for many months to several years but whenever they attempt to reduce or stop they get withdrawal symptoms. The longer they stay on tranquillisers the more difficult it seems to withdraw. Most of these people are on a relatively small dose and are in the frustrating position of wanting to stop yet being unable to do so without having withdrawal symptoms. They stay on the same dose more or less continuously.

A small proportion of dependent patients, about 1 per cent of the total who take tranquillisers, increase their intake steadily until they are taking many times the recommended dose. At these doses the drugs lose their effects quickly and more is needed because tolerance has developed. The patient is addicted.

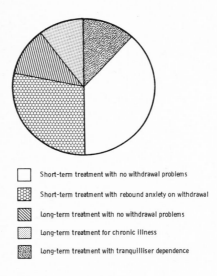

☐   Short-term treatment with no withdrawal problems

▦   Short-term treatment with rebound anxiety on withdrawal

▨   Long-term treatment with no withdrawal problems

▨   Long-term treatment for chronic illness

▦   Long-term treatment with tranquilliser dependence

Figure 1   Outcome of treatment with tranquillisers

If you have taken tranquillisers at any time in your life you belong to one of the six sections shown in Figure 1. The sections are not proportionately constant. As more people become aware of the dangers of *long-term* use of tranquillisers the sector indicating short-term treatment with no withdrawal problems should get larger and the others correspondingly smaller. In the past five years there has been a significant fall in the number of prescriptions for tranquillisers and more care is taken in their use. We are not going to remove the problem of tranquilliser dependence entirely but if doctors and the public work together with better awareness of the potential problems we can at least prevent much of the suffering that has been caused in the past and is still experienced by many patients.

2

Are you dependent on tranquillisers?

We saw at the end of Chapter 1 that people who take tranquillisers fall into six main groups. Much depends on the type of tablets taken. By far the largest group of tranquillisers is the benzodiazepines, but doctors may prescribe one of several other groups of drugs for the same purpose.

The following table shows which group various tranquillisers belong to. This is not a complete list however, so the drug you are taking may not be included.

All drugs used in medicine have to have an approved name which remains the same, wherever they are marketed throughout the world. This name often describes the chemical structure of the drug and is sometimes long and difficult to remember. The drug companies sell these drugs under trade names which are much simpler as they do not need to describe the nature of the drug. So only chemists and doctors tend to remember (and spell correctly) chlordiazepoxide, the first of the benzodiazepines to be used as a tranquilliser, but everyone remembers the name Librium.

In order to identify a drug, however, it is helpful to know the approved name as this will always stay the same whereas if several companies make the same drug they will each choose a different trade name for it. Also, they may alter the trade name if they sell the drug in different countries. What complicates matters even further is that the same drug manufactured under different trade names will look different as the tablets or capsules will be of another colour and have different markings, though the drug they contain will still be the same.

Beside each drug, the Table lists its risk of dependence, normal dosage and main use. Although all these drugs can be used as tranquillisers, for many their main use is quite different – as the Table shows. The fact that you are taking a drug included

Table 1 Drugs used mainly as tranquillisers or sleeping tablets

Type of drug	Approved name	Trade names	Dependence risk	Usual dose range (milli-grammes)	Main use
B E N Z O D I A Z E P I N E S	chlordiaze-poxide	Librium Tropium	moderate	10–30	anxiety
	diazepam	Valium, Atensine	moderate	5–20	anxiety
	lorazepam	Ativan	fairly high	2–7½	anxiety
	nitrazepam	Mogadon	moderate	5–20	insomnia
	temazepam	Euhypnos, Restoril	fairly high	10–40	insomnia
	flurazepam	Dalmane	moderate	15–30	insomnia
	clobazam	Frisium	moderate	10–40	anxiety, epilepsy
	oxazepam	Serenid forte, Serenid-D	fairly high	20–60	anxiety
	alprazolam	Xanax	fairly high	2–6	anxiety, anxiety with depression
	loprazolam	Dormonoct	fairly high	1–2	insomnia
	triazolam	Halcion	fairly high	⅛–¼	insomnia
	ketazolam	Anxon	moderate	15–45	insomnia
	prazepam	Centrax	moderate	10–30	anxiety
	lormetazepam	Noctamid Loramet	fairly high	½–1	insomnia
	bromazepam	Lexotan	fairly high	3–12	anxiety
	clorazepate	Tranxene	moderate	7½–30	anxiety & insomnia
	clonazepam	Rivotril	moderate	4–8	epilepsy
	medazepam	Nobrium	moderate	10–30	anxiety
	halazepam	Paxipam	moderate	40–160	anxiety
Barb-iturates and similar drugs	amylobarbi-tone	Sodium amytal	very high	100–400	insomnia
	quinalbarbitone	Tuinal	very high	100–400	insomnia
	glutethimide	Doriden	very high	250–500	insomnia
	primidone	Mysoline	low	750–1500	epilepsy
	phenobarbitone	Luminal	low	60–240	epilepsy
	alcohol	too many to mention	high	very variable	social reasons
Other tranqu-illisers	dichloral-phenazone	Welldorm	moderate	650–1950	insomnia
	chloral hydrate	Noctec	moderate	500–2000	insomnia
	meprobamate	Equanil	moderate	200–800	anxiety

13

Table 2   Drugs mainly used for other disorders but which have tranquillising properties

Type of drug	Approved name	Trade name	Dependence risk	Usual dose range (mg)	Main use
Anti-depress-ants	imipramine	Tofranil	very low	75–200	depression
	amitrip-tyline	Trypizol Elavil	very low	75–200	depression
	trimipramine	Surmontil	very low	75–200	depression
	dothiepin	Prothiaden	very low	75–200	depression
	desipramine	Pertofran	very low	75–200	depression
	protrip-tyline	Concordin	very low	15–40	depression
	mianserin	Bolvidon, Norval	very low	30–90	depression
	trazodone	Molipaxin	very low	75–200	depression
	viloxazine	Vivalan	very low	150–400	depression
Major tranquil-lisers	chlorpro-mazine	Largactil	none	200–1000	see text
	trifluo-perazine	Stelazine	none	10–15	see text
	prochlor-perazine	Stemetil Compazine	none	25–150	see text
	thiorida-zine	Melleril	none	100–500	see text
	flupen-thixol	Fluanxol, Depixol	none	1–9	see text
	haloperidol	Serenace Haldol	none	3–30	see text
Anti-hista-mines	promethazine	Phenergan Avomine	none	25–75	sea-sickness
	dimenhy-drinate	Dramamine	none	50–200	sea-sickness
	chlorphen-iramine	Piriton	none	4–12	allergies
Beta-blocking drugs	propranolol	Inderal	none	40–160	high blood pressure
	oxprenolol	Trasicor	none	80–320	high blood pressure

in Table 1 does not necessarily mean that it is being prescribed as a tranquilliser. If you are taking a benzodiazepine it *is* much more likely that it has been prescribed for a nervous problem, but even in this group, clonazepam and clobazam are now prescribed mainly for their benefits in epilepsy. The dosage range given refers to the main use of the drug.

Antidepressants are prescribed for depressive illnesses and major tranquillisers are given for serious mental disorders, mainly schizophrenia and manic depressive psychosis. However, when these drugs are used in lower dosage they have some tranquillising effects but little or no action on the condition for which they are mainly used. This is extremely important to remember because if, for example, you are taking a major tranquilliser such as chlorpromazine this does *not* imply that your doctor thinks you have schizophrenia but has decided not to tell you.

It is also frequent for people to be taking two different types of tranquilliser. It is particularly common for antidepressants and tranquillisers to be taken together, sometimes combined in one tablet. Tablets of this type are not included in the Table but the most common are Motival, Limbitrol and Triptafen. Limbitrol contains a benzodiazepine (chlordiazepoxide) and an anti-depressant (amitriptyline) and the other two are combinations of antidepressants and major tranquillisers in low dosage.

Alcohol is also included in the Tables (although now rarely prescribed by doctors) because it is worth reminding ourselves that alcohol is a drug and in many ways is very similar to the barbiturates. Nowadays barbiturates are seldom prescribed because they are dangerous in overdosage and so prone to dependence. If alcohol happened to be a new drug that was being considered for use on prescription there is no doubt that it would not be allowed because of its risks. It is only because alcohol is so much part of our society that it continues to be widely available.

In the United Kingdom many of the drugs in Tables 1 and 2 are no longer available on prescription due to recently imposed restrictions in prescribing. Only nine of the benzodiazepines: chlordiazepoxide, diazepam, lorazepam, nitrazepam, temazepam, oxazepam, loprazolam, lormetazepam and triazolam are still available by prescription for anxiety and insomnia on the National Health Service. It is quite likely that further restrictions wiil be introduced in the future.

Once you have identified the drugs you are taking from the Tables your chances of becoming dependent can be determined more accurately. The proportions of each group shown in the figure on page 10 are those for people taking benzodiazepines. If you are male and taking four pints of alcohol or its equivalent daily (or female and taking two and a half pints or more daily) your risks of chemical dependence are greater than if you were taking benzo-diazepines. The same applies to barbiturates when they are taken in regular dosage. In these cases the sectors of the circle showing no problems are much smaller and the ones indicating dependence much larger. In particular, the 1 per cent of patients who have severe dependence on benzodiazepines is multiplied many times in the case of barbiturate and alcohol dependence.

Conversely, if you are taking an antidepressant, an anti-histamine or major tranquilliser the likelihood of dependence is either very small indeed or non-existent.

The beta-blocking drugs are unusual because in the dosages used to treat anxiety they have no effect on the brain. They work by reducing physical symptoms of anxiety such as palpitations and trembling. In high doses they are used to treat high blood pressure but they have no effect on blood pressure in the low doses used to treat anxiety. Beta-blocking drugs also carry no risk of dependence.

Many of these other drugs with tranquillising properties have no risk of chemical dependence but that does not mean that people cannot come to rely on them, even to the extent of thinking that they are dependent. As noted earlier, even dummy pills can produce psychological dependence, and the same can apply for active drugs that are not addictive.

Problems when coming off tranquillisers

It may be helpful to give examples of the problems that people can have when coming off tranquillisers. These correspond to the various sectors in Figure 1. Each example comes from my clinical practice but has been altered slightly to avoid identification of the people concerned.

Group 1 – Short-term treatment with no dependence

Mrs Alexander came for help because of difficulty in getting to sleep. She had always slept well until three months previously. At that time she had been worried by problems connected with her work as a clerical officer in a government department. A new supervisor seemed to Mrs Alexander to criticize her unfairly for the standard and speed of her work. Mrs Alexander was too shy to stand up for herself under this criticism but could not forget about it when she returned home. Her preoccupations led to problems in her relationship with her husband who complained that she was moody and irritable.

Mrs Alexander was prescribed nitrazepam in a dose of between 5 mg and 10 mg (1–2 tablets) at night, with instructions to reduce to the lower dose as soon as possible. Although worried about taking sleeping tablets she took them as prescribed. She found that she still stayed awake for nearly three hours after taking only one tablet and increased to two the next night.

After a few days she felt a great deal better and her irritability disappeared. She was able to talk to her husband and he suggested ways of standing up to her supervisor. This gave her the confidence to express her point of view when next she was criticized unfairly. This seemed to have some effect, as the supervisor showed more respect and picked on her much less often.

Two weeks after starting nitrazepam Mrs Alexander was able to cut down the dose to half a tablet (2½ mg) at night and still slept well. By the end of the third week she found that the tablets were no longer necessary and stopped them altogether. Three months later she continued to sleep well and had no other problems. At no time during the reduction of tablets had she noticed any problems and this surprised her as she had heard about tranquilliser dependence before she started treatment.

Comment: Tranquillisers are often criticized because they treat symptoms rather than causes. This example – only one of many I could give – shows that this criticism is sometimes unfair. True, the nitrazepam only treated the insomnia, but because Mrs Alexander slept better she was more alert during the day and was able to work out a successful way of overcoming her problem without the need for any complex psychological treatment. Dependence was avoided by the short period of treatment, by taking the lowest effective dose of tablets and by the gradual reduction.

Group 2 – Temporary dependence (after short-term use)

Mr Baldwin worked as a salesman for a computer company. It was a small one but expanding rapidly and Mr Baldwin was encouraged to seek as many outlets as possible to increase sales. He had always been a somewhat anxious man but with the strain of the increased workload he found he could not relax at all. He was put on lorazepam tablets (1 mg) and advised to take between one and three a day. He found these a great help and when he took one tablet in the morning and one in the evening he was well throughout the day.

He increased his workload, received many new orders and was congratulated by his managing director. After five weeks his doctor encouraged him to reduce the tablets and as he had become so confident he decided to stop them altogether. He felt well the next day but on the morning after that he woke up panicky and tense. On the way to work he had an attack of shaking and sweating and afterwards felt very weak. He was tense throughout the day and could not concentrate. Over the next few days he was more anxious than usual but did not have any feelings of actual panic. Three weeks later he was coping well again though he still remained mildly anxious and on edge.

Comment: Mr Baldwin's symptoms after suddenly stopping lorazepam were those of anxiety and panic. As they came on just after stopping the tablets and lasted only a few days they were definite withdrawal symptoms even though they are also common in anxiety. Indeed, there is nothing particularly special about many withdrawal symptoms. Most are just the physical and psychological symptoms of anxiety but sometimes they may include more severe symptoms.

The symptoms were almost certainly shown because Mr Baldwin stopped the tablets suddenly. As we noted in Chapter 1, benzodiazepines bind with special receptors in the brain. When the tablets have been taken for a few weeks these receptors come to expect a regular supply of drug in the body and if it is removed suddenly there is a return of anxiety when the drugs are out of the system. Lorazepam is a short acting drug which is largely removed from the body after 24 hours. This explains why Mr Baldwin experienced his withdrawal symptoms on the very day after stopping his lorazepam.

Because his withdrawal symptoms were not particularly severe, Mr Baldwin was able to continue without taking the tablets and his symptoms gradually improved as the receptors in his brain adjusted to being without the lorazepam. Many people do not even notice these mild symptoms of withdrawal. It is only when they look back on the time they stopped their tablets that they realize that the violent temper, the panic attack, reluctance to go to the shopping centre or an inability to cope with the noise of the children, all happened just at the time they stopped their tablets.

Group 3 – Long-term use without dependence

Mr Carter is a 55-year-old man who hardly ever felt anxious and enjoyed perfect health until five years ago, when he had a heart attack and was in hospital for three weeks. He appeared to make a good recovery but found that whenever he did anything a little out of the ordinary he developed palpitations and became more nervous. His doctor put him on diazepam without specifying for how long the drug should be taken. Mr Carter improved and no longer had episodes of palpitations, but his doctor continued the prescription in a fairly low dose, 5 mg daily, by repeat prescription.

In the next five years Mr Carter often missed out his tablets but was reminded by his conscientious wife that he should continue his 'heart tablets' to avoid having further attacks. He was referred for further help mainly because he became concerned about the possibility of developing dependence. As he had no nervous symptoms at interview and had not seemed to have any the previous few months his dose was cut to half a tablet (2½ mg). Before his next appointment he decided to cut out the tablets altogether and did so without developing any withdrawal symptoms. He felt more alert after stopping his tablets and three weeks later proudly presented himself as cured.

Comment: It may not have been entirely appropriate for Mr Carter to take a benzodiazepine for his symptoms after his heart attack as a beta-blocking drug would have treated the palpitations directly. However, diazepam was helpful even though it should not have been continued for five years. As he was taking a relatively small dose it was also easier for him to reduce.

The changes in the brain receptors that seemed to account for Mr Baldwin's problems almost certainly occurred in Mr Carter as well, particularly as he had taken the drug for so much longer. But because Mr Carter had no anxious features in his normal personality the adjustments taking place in his brain after the drug was stopped did not lead to any withdrawal symptoms and he was able to avoid dependence despite having taken diazepam for several years.

Group 4 – Chronic use, chronic state

Mrs Dempster is fifty-four years old and has been taking sleeping tablets for twenty-eight years. She had suffered from insomnia since she was ten years old but did not take sleeping tablets until she was twenty-six. By that time she had three young children under the age of five and found that she could hardly sleep at all. Her doctor treated her with amylobarbitone sodium (Sodium amytal), a barbiturate, with immediate benefit. After two years he changed her prescription to dichloralphenazone (Welldorm) because he was concerned about the risks of continuing barbiturates. Mrs Dempster slept reasonably well on both the tablets prescribed in their turn but whenever she forgot to take the current medication her insomnia returned.

Then her tablets were changed to a new drug – thalidomide – which the doctor said was a great improvement on all existing sleeping tablets at that time. Fortunately, Mrs Dempster did not wish to have any more children and so was spared the terrible risks of pregnancy later associated with taking the drug. When thalidomide was shown to produce congenital abnormalities her tablet was changed to oxazepam and within three years to nitrazepam. Since then she has taken between one and two tablets (5–10 mg) every night.

Several doctors have suggested to Mrs Dempster that she no longer needs the tablets and should attempt to stop them. She always replies that as she sleeps well with the tablets and has no other problems she would like to continue taking them at night. She has no wish to return to the insomnia that handicapped her life for eighteen years before she started taking drugs. As she has never stopped her tablets for more than a single night it is impossible to tell whether she is chemically dependent. Because she does not want to reduce or stop the tablets four doctors who have tried at different times to get her to do so have resigned themselves to giving her repeat prescriptions.

Comment: Mrs Dempster probably *is* dependent on her sleeping tablets but as she has never stopped them long enough to have withdrawal symptoms it is impossible to tell. She has stayed on the same dose for many years so does not appear to have developed a significant amount of tolerance to the drug's effects. Continued prescription of the drug may be unnecessary but as she had insomnia for many years before she started taking sleeping tablets it may be that she genuinely belongs to a relatively small group of people who are chronic insomniacs. Because she is so unwilling to reduce and then stop her tablets it is not surprising that the doctors who have seen her have decided to continue her prescriptions.

This may indeed be the best option. The only reason for demanding that she reduces her tablets is evidence of definite harm if she continues to take them. She has no important side-effects from her tablets and is not increasing the dose. The doctors have warned her about the dangers of taking alcohol with the sleeping tablets and reminded her that they produce a hangover effect the next day which would affect her co-ordination and speed of reaction. She follows the advice about alcohol and still maintains that she would rather continue on the tablets unless there is some reason that prohibits it absolutely.

There has been some concern about benzodiazepines causing some permanent damage to brain functioning after they have been taken for some years (see Chapter 7). This is a controversial subject and the scientists working on it have produced conflicting results. At present it cannot be said that any tranquilliser produces a permanent effect on brain functioning and certainly long-term use of the tablets could not be banned for this reason. Mrs Dempster represents a much larger group than many realize, and you will note from Figure 1 on page 10 that people in this group account for about one in ten of people taking tranquillisers.

Group 5 – Full dependence syndrome

Mr Edwards is a happily married man of forty-one with two children. He has always regarded himself as more anxious than most people but felt this was because he had very high standards and it distressed him when others did not match up to these.

He had always been close to his mother and when she developed bone cancer fourteen years ago he could not stop worrying about her. When he went to his doctor he was prescribed chlordiazepoxide (Librium) 10 mg three times a day and felt better. This prescription was changed to diazepam by his doctor shortly afterwards when Librium did not seem quite so effective. He took a 5 mg dose three to four times a day and soon was able to reduce to 10 mg daily. When his mother died three years later he temporarily increased to 15 mg daily before returning to his usual 10 mg dose. As he began to feel much better he tried reducing his tablets but each time he did so he developed tension and twitching in the muscles, attacks of panic and insomnia. This made him return to his normal dose again.

After nine years on the tablets Mr Edwards was referred for specialist help. He agreed to take part in a withdrawal programme which involved replacing his 5 mg tablets with 2 mg ones and then reducing steadily over eight weeks. This seemed to go well at first but after four weeks he became more tense and had a return of his muscle twitching. He had attacks of shaking followed by nausea and felt dizzy whenever he went out. At times he felt his legs were turning to jelly or that they weighed many tons. As he felt he could not continue having these symptoms over the next four weeks he decided to stop the tablets altogether in order to 'shorten the agony'.

This withdrawal led to a new set of symptoms. Not only was he still panicky and on edge all the time but he felt that his family and friends were against him. He even stopped confiding in his wife as he thought she was making fun of him behind his back. He stopped going out of the house because when he walked down the road he felt as though he was on board a ship on a rough sea. The buildings seemed to sway from side to side, daylight seemed so intense it seemed to flash and hurt his eyes and even the noise of traffic was excruciating.

Five days after stopping his tablets altogether Mr Edwards had an epileptic fit while sitting at home. His wife saw him go rigid, stop breathing and then shake all over; she thought he was dying. When seen by the doctor he had recovered consciousness and could not remember what had happened. He had never had epileptic fits before and when hospital tests were made they showed normal brain function. On the advice of the specialist, he returned to the reducing programme and after four weeks was surprised to find things gradually improving. He still felt tense but no longer had such unpleasant sensations.

Over the next six months Mr Edwards stayed tense and nervous, with disturbed sleep and occasional episodes of trembling. He was determined not to return to taking tranquillisers because in other ways he felt so much better without them. He was more alert and said, 'It is as though I have been walking in a fog for years without knowing it and it's so nice to be in the open air again.'

Although he expected to remain anxious over the next year this also improved. He was able to cope with stresses much more effectively and when one of his children had a road accident and went into hospital he surprised his wife by taking over responsibility from her. She had always felt the need to support him at times of stress and now he was supporting her. Three years later he remains well and is a valuable member of a volunteer group helping other people to stop taking tranquillisers.

Comment: Even if no other evidence was available Mr Edwards' experiences show that tranquillisers can produce chemical dependence. When he first started reducing the tablets the main symptoms he had were those of anxiety and, in themselves, these do not necessarily mean that he was dependent. It could be that these symptoms were just a return of his 'normal' anxiety that bothered him before starting tranquillisers. However, when he developed the abnormal perceptions that led him to believe that his senses were playing tricks on him, these feelings were outside his normal range of experience.

He made a mistake in stopping his tablets without consultation but one can understand his feelings at the time. He felt he would rather get it over with quickly than drag out the withdrawal symptoms for several more weeks. Unfortunately, this made the symptoms worse and he had one of the most serious possible withdrawal reactions, an epileptic fit.

When he returned to the withdrawal programme Mr Edwards' symptoms slowly, but steadily, improved. This is also the common pattern of a true withdrawal reaction. Symptoms reach a peak within two or three days after stopping a short acting drug such as lorazepam and about a week after stopping a long-acting drug. Diazepam, after regular dosage, should be treated as a long-acting drug because it is transformed (metabolized) into a long-acting drug when it has been taken for a few days in regular dosage. With a long-acting drug the symptoms take longer to disperse and it may be several weeks after the last tablet has been taken before the drug is completely cleared from the body.

Mr Edwards' higher level of anxiety after the withdrawal symptoms were over is also fairly typical. After many years on tranquillisers the normal ways of coping with stress that the body carries out automatically fall into disuse. The recovered addict therefore has to learn how to cope with stress all over again and it can take several months. This is what Mr Edwards found. Although he was prepared to tolerate his higher level of tension because he felt so much more alert, he was surprised to find that even this symptom disappeared in time.

There are therefore two parts to the withdrawal syndrome after long-term use. The first is a short period, coming on during withdrawal and lasting for up to four weeks after the tablets have been stopped completely. The second is a longer period of several months during which time there is no drug circulating in the body but its after-effects are still present.

Group 6 – Rising dependence

Mrs Fairfax was a 36-year-old mother of four children who had taken illegal drugs since she was twenty. She was what is often called a polydrug user, taking whatever addictive drug was available but rarely for long in regular dosage. At various times she had taken amphetamines, methadone, heroin and LSD. Her husband had also taken similar drugs in the past and had been in prison for theft and burglary. Because she was told that the drugs might damage unborn children she made a determined effort to stop taking them during her third pregnancy. She succeeded and for two years took no drugs of any sort.

Unfortunately, her husband continued his illegal activities and was arrested again following another robbery. Mrs Fairfax was shocked and surprised by this and became distressed. She was prescribed a sleeping tablet, temazepam, by her doctor and at first took this as prescribed in a dose of 20 mg at night. Within a few weeks, however, she had increased her daily dose to 80 mg a day, only a small proportion of which she was taking at night. The tablets no longer had the same effect and as her doctor would not prescribe more she obtained temazepam illegally.

Within a few weeks she was taking 20 tablets (280 mg) a day in order to stay both calm and relaxed and to sleep well. Despite taking this excessive dose she was not at all drowsy at interview.

Mrs Fairfax was referred for specialist help and, on close questioning, admitted the full extent of her drug taking. She agreed to attend a day hospital and for her drugs to be reduced steadily over a three week period. At first this failed because she continued to get illegal supplies of drugs but after six months she had been withdrawn from temazepam completely.

There were four withdrawal attempts during this period during each of which she developed acute attacks of panic associated with tightness in the chest. During these she breathed more heavily and rapidly and had tingling in her hands and feet. She also developed severe craving for temazepam and at first could only satisfy this by getting illegal supplies.

Later in withdrawal she was troubled by feelings of unreality. She felt cut off from the world, as if she was imprisoned in a cinema and everything around her was not real but only being shown on film. At times this feeling became so intense she thought she was going mad. None of her friends seemed to understand her feelings and just said that she would get over it.

Soon afterwards her husband was released from prison and the family was together again. This reinforced Mrs Fairfax's determination to stay off her drugs. Two months later she was coping well and had no significant anxiety symptoms although she still had some difficulty in getting off to sleep.

Comment: Rising dependence is rare with the benzodiazepines but more common with barbiturates and alcohol. Once the dose of tablets is increased beyond the normal range, tolerance develops quickly and more and more of the drug is needed to produce the desired effect. In Mrs Fairfax's case her previous abuse of drugs probably encouraged her to use temazepam in the same way. Within a few weeks she was taking a daily dosage that would have rendered her unconscious had it been taken at the beginning of therapy. The same applies with barbiturates and alcohol when they are taken in this way. At this level of dependence, craving is much more common and the person will do almost anything to get hold of the drug as nothing else seems to relieve the symptoms.

Mrs Fairfax also had symptoms of panic and even began to feel unreal. Panic affects people in different ways but in almost all instances it includes physical symptoms such as:

- trembling
- palpitations
- difficulty in breathing
- tightness of the chest
- flushing
- sweating
- nausea.

When tightness of the chest is a main problem the person responds by breathing more quickly. This removes important gases from the lungs too quickly and the body chemistry is disturbed. This accounts for the tingling in the hands, feet and other parts of the body that sometimes occurs during withdrawal. It is important to realize that these symptoms are caused by panic and over-breathing rather than being symptoms that can only occur during withdrawal.

The feeling of unreality that Mrs Fairfax described is technically known as depersonalization if it applies to the person concerned, and derealization if it is the outside world that seems to be unreal. It can also occur in attacks of anxiety but is common as a withdrawal symptom. Because it is such an odd feeling people who experience it quite frequently fear that they might be losing their mind. In fact, if you get this symptom during withdrawal you can rest assured that this will not happen.

That covers almost all the reactions that can occur after withdrawal of a tranquillising drug, but there is another possibility that takes place in about 20 per cent of people when they are reducing tranquillisers. It is best described as false dependence and is illustrated by the following case history.

Group 7: False dependence

Ms Goodhead is a 28-year-old unmarried lady who had taken chlordiazepoxide (Librium) for eight years, but had not always taken it regularly and sometimes stopped taking it for several weeks at a time. She had always been concerned about her health and was alarmed to read in a magazine that diazepam and other benzodiazepines could cause chemical dependence. Ms Goodhead found that she could no longer stop her tablets and began taking 30 mg regularly every day. Three months later she was referred for specialist help and agreed to take part in a withdrawal programme although she felt it unlikely to work as she was so hopelessly addicted.

Librium has only two standard dosage strengths: 5 mg and 10 mg, but special supplies for patients coming off this tablet include a lower strength of 2 mg. Ms Goodhead was asked to reduce to the lowest possible dose using her own supply of tablets but found she could not get below 25 mg daily. At this point she was switched over to the new tablets, and advised to take two 10 mg tablets and two 2 mg tablets daily, thus reducing by a mere 1 mg more.

Two weeks later she returned to the clinic saying she had experienced severe withdrawal symptoms. In addition to feelings of panic, difficulty in sleeping, restlessness, confusion, twitching in the muscles, weakness in the limbs and increased sensations she had also developed fever, a vaginal discharge, pains in her joints and hair loss. She claimed that almost without exception these symptoms were new and therefore must be those of withdrawal.

However, this claim was thought to be false interpretation. She had only reduced by 1 mg and yet had developed a whole range of apparently new symptoms. To test whether this was a case of false interpretation, she was persuaded to continue on the same number of tablets but first one 2 mg tablet was replaced with a dummy pill (placebo) and later the second one was replaced by a dummy pill also. Four weeks later, though unaware of this much greater reduction, she was taking only 20 mg daily. She had no new symptoms during this time and many of the other ones improved. So, using similar deception, her stronger tablets of Librium were also replaced by dummy pills.

By the end of two months Ms Goodhead was taking no active tablets. It was then explained to her that she had been successful in coming off her tablets without realizing it and that the tablets she was now taking contained only sugar (lactose). Over the next few days she had a temporary increase in symptoms but these resolved and one month later she remained without tablets and with no symptoms apart from insomnia.

Comment: This patient illustrates a problem that is now more common as people become aware of tranquilliser dependence. It can be seen as one of the many examples of Murphy's Law: 'if withdrawal symptoms can happen after reducing tranquillisers, they will happen.' The increase in symptoms that Ms Goodhead noticed after changing over her tablets occurred largely because she expected these symptoms – and because she expected them they duly appeared. Conversely, when the tablets were reduced without her knowledge she did not develop withdrawal symptoms.

It may seem unfair for doctors to conceal from patients the fact that they are changing over to a dummy pill but it is the only way of telling whether withdrawal symptoms *are* indications of chemical dependence or whether they are just a form of psychological dependence. In fact, most people stopping tranquillisers are not easily fooled. Only about one in five get symptoms like those of Ms Goodhead when they are not really reducing their tablets to any significant degree.

Summary

False dependence can occur with any of the six other groups described and is now more common than it used to be because so many people are aware of the problems of tranquilliser dependence.

The message of false dependence is simple: do not assume that you will develop new symptoms when you reduce your tablets because, if you do, any true withdrawal symptoms you develop will be made worse and you may also experience new symptoms that are nothing to do with the reduction of your tablets. It is all too easy to blame all your symptoms on tranquilliser withdrawal, because this means that you will bear no personal responsibility for them. Tranquilliser dependence is a major problem but it *never* accounts for all the difficulties in people's lives and neither will it solve them.

By now you should be able to work out to which group of tranquillisers you belong. It is important that you are honest with yourself when making this decision because it will determine the type of withdrawal programme that you undertake. There is a natural tendency for all of us to choose the option that puts us in the most favourable light, but if you choose the wrong group this will not help you when you start your withdrawal.

3

How to Reduce Tranquillisers

We now have enough information to decide some general principles when reducing tranquillisers. The first thing to remember is that there are important differences between the effects of a drug when it it is taken just once or twice and when it is taken in regular dosage for several weeks. When a drug is taken for the first time it starts showing its effects as soon as it is absorbed into the blood system. These effects last for between a few minutes and many hours, after which the drug is broken down and no longer has any significant action. There is a technical term – half-life – used to describe the length of time it takes for half of a dose of the drug to be eliminated from the body. In most cases this period is approximately the same as the length of action of the drug and, for the people who take the drugs, this is the most important thing to measure.

Deciding the reduction rate

If a drug is taken once or twice only or is taken occasionally (that is, once or twice a week) there is no harm in stopping suddenly. However, if the drug is taken regularly for a week or longer changes take place in the nervous system as it adapts to the presence of the new drug. These changes are gradual but once they have occurred it is important to reduce the tablets slowly so that the nervous system can adjust again, only this time in the opposite way to when the drug was being taken regularly. If the drug is stopped suddenly the nervous system cannot adapt in this way quickly enough. In mild cases this leads to what is called 'rebound anxiety'. In more severe cases it shows as a definite withdrawal syndrome.

It is therefore wise, after regular dosage, to allow the nervous system to adapt by reducing at a rate that prevents the occurrence of rebound anxiety and withdrawal symptoms. This

31

reduction rate varies with different drugs. For example, although all benzodiazepines are very similar, the speed at which they are broken down differs. And some drugs which are broken down quickly are then converted into others that are just as active as the original. In general, the faster the drug is broken down the more gradual should be its reduction.

The benzodiazepines can be divided into three groups:

- those with a long duration of action (more than 40 hours)
- medium duration (10–40 hours)
- short duration (less than 10 hours).

Table 3   Differences between benzodiazepines and their recommended speed of withdrawal

Benzodiazepine	Duration of action	Speed of withdrawal	Recommended maximum daily dose before controlled withdrawal (mg)
alprazolam	medium	moderate	3
bromazepam	medium	moderate	9
chlordiazepoxide	long	fast	20
clobazam	long	fast	20
clonazepam	long	fast	15
clorazepate	long	fast	15
diazepam	long	fast	15
halazepam	medium	moderate	10
ketazolam	long	fast	30
loprazolam	medium	moderate	2
lorazepam	short	moderate	3
lormetazepam	short	slow	1
medazepam	long	fast	20
nitrazepam	long	fast	10
oxazepam	short	slow	20
prazepam	long	fast	30
temazepam	short	slow	20
triazolam	short	slow	¼

The recommended speed of withdrawal depends on which class your tranquilliser belongs. The different groups are summarized in Table 3.

As benzodiazepines form by far the largest group of tranquillisers they receive most attention in this book but if you are taking one of the other tranquillisers mentioned in Table 2 the same principles still apply. Most of the drugs should be reduced at approximately the same rate as the medium-acting benzodiazepines. However, before deciding on reduction be quite sure that there is no special reason for you to continue the tablets. If you are taking the drugs simply to relieve tension and anxiety or to help you to sleep, it is quite reasonable for you to consider reducing them on your own. On the other hand, if you have a medical condition such as epilepsy it may be quite inappropriate for you to reduce the tablets. If you have any doubt about this do consult your doctor before attempting any form of withdrawal.

Table 3 shows the maximum daily dose that should be taken before considering controlled withdrawal. The reason for this will become apparent later but even at this stage it will be clear that there are likely to be more problems in withdrawing from a high dose of tablets than from a low one. In our controlled withdrawal programmes we usually find that people cannot complete these satisfactorily if, at the start of the programme, they are taking too high a dose of tablets – that is, a dose higher than the relevant one mentioned in Table 3. Our practice is to recommend that the dosage is reduced to at least the highest level for that particular tablet given in Table 3 before taking part in a formal withdrawal programme.

You will note some important differences between the figures mentioned in Tables 1 and 3. For example, the usual dosage range of diazepam and nitrazepam are the same in Table 1 but different in Table 3. This is because a benzodiazepine given for anxiety in one dose is extremely good at helping insomnia in a slightly larger dose: 5 mg of diazepam is equivalent to approximately 3 mg of nitrazepam and it is only because nitrazepam is given for insomnia that its dosage range is about the same as that of diazepam.

Six important factors

In the next two chapters separate withdrawal programmes are described. The programme for you will depend on six main factors. These are:

- the type of drug
- its dosage
- duration of use
- previous withdrawal symptoms
- life problems
- personality.

It will help you to have pen and paper available as we go through each of these as your total score will determine whether you should use the rapid or slow withdrawal programme. Alternatively, you may prefer to put your score for each item in the boxes on the right of the page.

Type of drug

By this stage you should know to which class the drug you are taking belongs. The drug may not have been mentioned specifically but it is likely that the class to which it belongs has been described. If not, it could be that your drug is not a tranquilliser. For example, aspirin and other pain killers are sometimes taken regularly for headaches and other forms of tension that may be due to anxiety. Aspirin is not addictive but some of the stronger pain killers – including opium, morphine and heroin – *are* major drugs of abuse. If you are taking one of these you may find some useful advice in this book but the withdrawal programmes are not necessarily appropriate for you. The drug you are taking may also not have been mentioned because it is a new compound. Because of concern over the benzodiazepines many drug companies are bringing out new compounds that are not benzodiazepines. In general, these are less likely to produce dependence but despite the stringent testing required by law it is impossible to be sure until they have been in general use for some time.

If you are taking an antihistamine, an antidepressant, a major tranquilliser or a beta-blocking drug give yourself a score of 0.

If you are taking phenobarbitone, mysoline, meprobamate, dichloralphenazone or chloral hydrate give yourself a score of 1 in box one.

Box 1

All the medium or long duration benzodiazepines given in Table 3 receive a score of 2.

Other benzodiazepines, other barbiturates and alcohol (equivalent of 4 pints a day or more) receive a score of 3.

If you are taking a combination of tranquillisers your score is that indicated for the drug which has the highest number. (For example, if you are taking an antihistamine but drinking 5 pints a day regularly your score will be 3.)

Dosage

Add up your total daily dosage in milligrammes. If you only take the tablet occasionally and for less than three days each week or longer, score 0.

If you are taking a benzodiazepine in an average daily dosage which is the same as, or lower than that given in Table 3, score 1 in box 2.

Box 2

If you are not taking a benzodiazepine consult the dosage range given in Table 2. If your average daily dose is less than 50 per cent higher than the first of the numbers given in the dosage range then score 1. All others should score 2 except those taking the higher doses of beta-blocking drugs, major tranquillisers and antidepressants. If you are in this last group it is quite likely that you are not taking your tablets just for a nervous problem. You should make further enquiries before going through a withdrawal programme and score 1.

Duration of use

Calculate how long you have taken the tablets regularly.

If you do not need to take the tablets for three days each week or more score 0 in box 3.

Also give yourself a score of 0 if you have taken the drug for four weeks or less in regular dosage.

Box 3

For between 1 and 4 months regular use, score 1.
Between 4 and 12 months, score 2.
For longer than 12 months, score 3. However, do not bother to score this item if you are taking an antidepressant, a major tranquilliser, an antihistamine or a beta-blocking drug. Many people feel that they must be more addicted to a drug if they have taken it for, say, 20 years than if they have taken it for five years.

Table 4 List of withdrawal symptoms after reducing or stopping tranquillisers

Mild withdrawal symptoms	Severe withdrawal symptoms	Unlikely or false withdrawal symptoms
insomnia	severe depression	severe joint pains
muscle tension	muscle twitching	incontinence of urine
sweating	burning sensations in the skin	tinnitus
trembling	hallucinations	vomiting
dizziness	paranoid symptoms	thought control
headaches	confusion and memory loss	missing heart beats
nausea	delusions	loss of hair
loss of appetite		
blurred vision	epileptic fits	obesity
phobias		
increased sensitivity to noise and light	impressions of objects moving when they are still	allergy to foods
weakness in arms and legs	unreality (depersonalisation and derealisation)	skin rashes
panic		
tingling in hands and feet		
loss of interest		
inability to concentrate		

This is not the case, although when a drug has been taken for a long time there is a greater likelihood of psychological and false dependence.

Previous withdrawal symptoms

Table 4 lists the symptoms that can occur after reducing or stopping tranquillisers. Look at these carefully and tick off those that apply to you. *Do not* include feelings that you have had regularly while taking the tranquillisers as these cannot be withdrawal symptoms unless they become a great deal worse and different in quality after withdrawal. Do not be put off by the Table headings. The term 'mild withdrawal symptoms' does not mean that the symptoms are necessarily mild; it only indicates that these symptoms are very common in states of anxiety and so you should not regard them as withdrawal symptoms only.

Most of these symptoms have been described earlier but some require further explanation:

- Hallucinations describe the impression of seeing or hearing things that are not actually there. For example, one lady who was reducing tranquillisers was convinced that voices were talking to her from her hair dryer and other electrical appliances in the house when she was going through the peak of withdrawal symptoms. People can sometimes have visions as well but these are rarely frightening except during alcohol withdrawal.

- Paranoid symptoms include feelings of persecution and the conviction that others are talking about you behind your back. Sometimes they can be so serious that the person undergoing withdrawal is convinced that others are plotting to harm, or even kill, him. Delusions describe false beliefs of this sort that the person insists are true despite all evidence to the contrary.

The last column of Table 4 lists unlikely or false withdrawal symptoms. These are not part of tranquilliser dependence and you should look for other explanations for the symptoms rather than regard them as imaginary:

- If you notice severe joint pains and fever when withdrawing from tranquillisers it could be that you have a form of arthritis that needs medical attention. There is a tendency sometimes to blame all new symptoms on withdrawal and this could hide some important medical conditions.

- Tinnitus describes noises in the ears and can have many causes but drug withdrawal is rarely one of them.
- Although nausea and diarrhoea can sometimes occur during withdrawal actual vomiting is rare and if all three come together it is more likely that you have a stomach infection than a withdrawal syndrome.
- Some people also blame weight gain on withdrawal symptoms. In fact, as can be seen in column one of Table 4, loss of appetite is an important symptom when reducing tranquillisers. It is not possible to have loss of appetite and also gain weight unless you are forcing yourself to eat more. Most people lose up to half a stone when reducing tranquillisers if they are dependent and this can be an added bonus to those who are already overweight.

If you have had no problems when withdrawing tranquillisers in the past or fewer than three of the symptoms described under mild withdrawal, score 0 in box 4.

Box 4 If you have three or more of the mild withdrawal symptoms and/or one or two of the severe withdrawal symptoms, score 1.

If you have three or more of the severe withdrawal symptoms, score 2.

Life problems

None of us can avoid problems altogether in our day to day living but some have more difficulty than others. As might be expected, the best time to withdraw from tranquillisers is when you can be reasonably sure of a period of stability and calm in your life. This should apply to your occupation (or other regular activities if you are unemployed), your personal and family relationships, and spare time activities. Anxiety has a great deal to do with uncertainty and if you have reason to worry in your life it is going to be more difficult for you when you reduce your tranquillisers.

Box 5 Give yourself a score of 0 in box 5 if you feel you are able to

achieve this period of stability.
If you feel it is going to be impossible, score 1.

Personality

It is extremely difficult for us to describe our own personality because we do not have the gift of seeing ourselves as others see us. Personality sometimes appears to change when people are taking tranquillisers and if you have been on them for many years it is usually difficult to remember how you were before this time. Nevertheless, try to recall the sort of person you were before you started on your tablets, enrolling the help of friends and relatives if necessary. There are many different parts to a personality but the main features associated with difficulties in stopping tranquillisers are given in Table 5.

Table 5   Personality features associated with difficulties in stopping tranquillisers

Personality feature
always worrying
needing support from others
difficulty in adapting to change
moodiness
giving in to others
never able to relax
concern over health

None of these features are positive ones that we would like to possess but look at yourself coolly and honestly before scoring. If you have two or more of these features, score 1 in box 6, Otherwise, score 0.

Box 6

Dependence score

Now, add up the scores for each of the six factors determining the withdrawal programme and put the total in box 7. We will call this the dependence score.
If your total score is less than 2 you should have no difficulty in

Box 7

stopping your tablets and you might as well do this without a formal programme. At this stage you are not addicted and so have nothing to worry about.

If your score is between 2 and 6, go through the rapid withdrawal programme described in chapter 4.

If your score is between 7 and 10 the slow withdrawal programme described in chapter 5 should be more appropriate for you.

If you have the two top scores of 11 or 12 you should also try the slow withdrawal programme but are likely to have major difficulties. You *might* belong to group four described on page 20, even though you differ from Mrs Dempster in at least wanting to stop taking your tranquillisers. The additional treatments detailed in Chapter 6 will probably be necessary for you.

4

Rapid Withdrawal Programme

In this programme it is assumed that you do not have a severe problem with dependence on tranquillisers and should be able to withdraw fairly quickly without the need for any specialist assistance. You can go ahead on your own after taking a few important precautions:

- You should be absolutely certain that there is no medical reason for you to continue taking the tranquillisers. If there is no medical reason and you are taking them simply for anxiety or insomnia, your doctor will only be too pleased for you to attempt withdrawal on your own.
- Try to choose a time when no unusual stresses are likely before starting withdrawal.
- You should not be taking more than the dosages of benzo-diazepines given in Table 3 when you start your reduction programme. In almost all instances this will mean that you are not taking more than three tablets a day but because some drug companies market their tablet in much lower dosage than others, you *could* be taking four or more tablets a day yet still remain within the Table 3 limits. This does not matter but you will have to take more care in interpreting the programme outlined in Table 6 because, although the dosage will be correct, the numbers of tablets will be wrong.

How to reduce your tablets or capsules

Table 6 is only a guide to withdrawal; you need not stick to it absolutely. There are different rates of reduction depending on the number of tablets you are taking daily. The principles behind the reduction rate are:

- To cut down the number of times you take the tablets in the day as much as possible.

41

Table 6 Rapid withdrawal programme for stopping tranquillisers

'alt' is short for 'alternate days'. So '½ alt' means that you take ½ a tablet on Monday, Wednesday, Friday and Sunday and none on Tuesday, Thursday and Saturday. See page 44 for the withdrawal programme for those who take sleeping tablets only.

	Week	Total tablets/ wk	Morning	Midday	Evening	Spare tablets/wk
Starting dose 1 tablet/day	1	18½	1	½	1	1
	2	16	1	nil	1	2
	3	13½	½	nil	1	3
	4	11	½ alt	nil	1	2
	5	8½	nil	nil	1	1½
	6	6	nil	nil	1 alt, ½ alt	1
	7	4	nil	nil	½	½
	8	2	nil	nil	½ alt	½
	9	0	nil	nil	nil	nil
Starting dose 2 tablets/day	1	12	½	nil	1	1½
	2	10	½ alt	nil	1	1
	3	8	nil	nil	1	1
	4	6	nil	nil	1 alt, ½ alt	½
	5	4	nil	nil	½	½
	6	2	nil	nil	½ alt	½
	7	1	nil	nil	nil	1
	8	0	nil	nil	nil	nil
Starting dose 3 tablets/day	1	5½	½ alt	nil	½	½
	2	4	nil	nil	½	½
	3	3	nil	nil	½ alt	1
	4	2	nil	nil	½ alt	½
	5	1	nil	nil	nil	1
	6	0	nil	nil	nil	nil

- To reduce more quickly at first than later.
- To have spare tablets available for emergencies when you feel more anxious.

The reason for retaining a few spare tablets is that anxiety and insomnia are not predictable and constant. The same applies to withdrawal symptoms. Sometimes they seem intolerable after only a tiny reduction in tablets and yet may disappear altogether when a much larger reduction is made. Rather than work out the perfect rate of reduction it is better to have a tablet or two available for emergencies to cope with a sudden and unexpected surge in symptoms.

Each time you take a tablet there is the expectation that it will do some good and you often feel better even before the tablet is absorbed into your system. The same applies with psychological dependence. In general, therefore, people who takes tablets only at night for sleeping should find it easier to stop their tablets than those who take them several times a day for anxiety. As people on sleeping tablets take them in higher dosage, however, this difference is not always shown. This also explains why it is usually preferable to reduce more slowly at the *end* of the withdrawal programme. The best approach is to set aside the total number of tablets you will need for each week's reduction programme. Then follow the programme and take the spare tablets only if necessary. At the end of that week it is best to throw away the spare tablets in case you are tempted to take them the next week, although you may incorporate them into next week's quota if you wish. It is also important to keep all tablets in sealed containers and away from children.

At various points in the programme you will need to take either one tablet or half a tablet on alternate days. Some people prefer to cut the tablets into quarters. This is quite in order but do bear in mind that most tablets are only designed to be cut in half and when you cut them into smaller portions you always lose a certain amount as each tablet crumbles. One of my patients tried to overcome this problem by grinding down his weekly supply and separating the powder into equal portions. But this is not recommended as sometimes it can alter the chemical action of the drug.

People who are taking capsules rather than tablets will also have problems because capsules cannot be cut in half. Again, they may be tempted to do this but it is not recommended, particularly when they contain a liquid. It may be possible for the capsule to be replaced by tablet of equal strength but, if not, the reduction programme of Table 6 will have to be modified slightly. It will also need modification for those who only take tablets once a day, as will apply to all people who just take sleeping tablets. The simple solution is to add together the morning, midday and evening dose indicated, to give a single total and reduce according to that figure. There is no point in increasing the number of times you take a tablet each day for the purpose of a reducing programme.

The final modification involves those who are taking more than three tablets a day because the dosage is of a low strength. Provided that the total dose is less than that given in Table 3, think of each of your tablets as a half-strength dose. This will make it easier for you to reduce smoothly as, for example, when you come across the instruction 'half alt' you can continue on half a tablet daily instead of a half on alternate days.

People who do not develop withdrawal symptoms to any degree may find the rate of reduction given in Table 6 too slow. They will be impatient to reduce more rapidly and there is no reason why they should not do so. However, they should be careful not to reduce *too* rapidly. It is recommended that twice the rate of reduction shown in Table 6 is the maximum that should be tried. This means that the even numbered weeks in Table 6 can be missed out and reduction will be complete by the end of four weeks.

Problems during withdrawal

Once started on the withdrawal programme do not be tempted to change it substantially. The provision of spare tablets will allow you to make minor changes but it is unwise to go beyond this as there is a danger that you will lose heart and find your dosage increasing again. The only exception is when an unexpected stress comes along in the middle of your reducing programme. If this happens you can suspend reduction for a maximum of two weeks or return to the original dose, depending on how far you have reduced at the time the stress occurs.

Remember that even after you have completed withdrawal you may feel a bit more anxious than usual because you still need time to relearn how to cope with stresses. Do not be disappointed if you are troubled by symptoms at this time because there is every chance that they will improve over the next month or two. It will help a great deal if your friends and relatives also know about your reducing programme. They will then be able to make allowances for any anxiety or irritability that you may show during the withdrawal process. They also may be able to give you invaluable support when you are feeling a little demoralized. There is seldom any need to give up work in order to go through the rapid withdrawal programme but some people prefer to withdraw during their holidays when there are less stresses in their lives. I will leave this to you, and whatever method and approach you use, may I wish you the best of luck.

What to do if the programme fails

What has gone wrong? You have a low dependence score and should be able to complete rapid withdrawal successfully. A common problem in going through the withdrawal programme is a 'honeymoon period' after beginning reduction when all goes well. This can produce the smug, satisfied notion that you have a tough constitution and that you are going to beat this dependence without any problems. Then, suddenly, you come down with a bump. At some point in the withdrawal programme – it can happen at any stage – you develop serious symptoms and cannot tolerate them. You feel demoralized and cheated and return to taking your full dose of tranquillisers.

There is no reason why you should not try again when you have recovered your nerve. Try to work out why the programme failed

– and do not jump to the automatic conclusion that you must be more addicted than you thought. Alternatively you can transfer to the slow withdrawal programme described in the next chapter. This allows more flexibility and control when reducing. If you have to do this do not regard yourself as inadequate or a hopeless case. You have several choices ahead of you. This is only round one and many worthy fighters do not win in the first round.

5

Slow Withdrawal Programme

Most of you who try the slow withdrawal programme will have tried before to reduce unsuccessfully, know all about withdrawal symptoms, have a high dependence score (see Chapter 3) and are probably feeling fairly pessimistic. You seem to have tried everything and yet the pills have not let you escape from their clutches.

You are in control

This programme is different. You are going to control your own withdrawal programme and can take as long as you like. There is no need to feel that you are being forced to follow a system that is not made for you. The programme is worked out from your answers to the following seven questions.

Do you want to give up taking tranquillisers now?

You may think this is a silly question as you would not be reading these words if you did not want to give up tranquillisers. But the important word is 'now'. If you are contemplating a slow withdrawal programme it is almost certain that you have had withdrawal symptoms in the recent past and may not have the stomach to start withdrawing again. Remember that however you feel before you start withdrawal you are going to feel worse before you feel better. Are you prepared for this and can you accept the consequences?

If you are not really motivated and determined you will chicken out when the going gets rough and the programme will fail. You therefore need to choose a time when you are optimistic that you can stop taking tranquillisers, are strong enough to cope with an increase in symptoms, and are prepared to stick to your programme through to the end. Try to be honest with yourself when answering this question. It will save a lot of trouble later on.

How long do you wish to take over withdrawal?

Take into account your previous attempts at withdrawal. You need to compromise between the advantages of a short withdrawal period, which concentrates the withdrawal symptoms so that you suffer them for less time, and a long withdrawal period, which is associated with less intense symptoms but lengthens the period in which you experience them. A suitable time range is between two months and one year.

If you could stop your tranquillisers in less than two months you would not be contemplating the slow withdrawal programme; on the other hand, you would need the patience and persistence of Job to extend a withdrawal programme for longer than a year.

One disadvantage of all withdrawal programmes is that they encourage people to pay more attention to their symptoms for the period of withdrawal.

Most people find this acceptable over a short period but when it becomes extended over many months the significance of the symptoms may be exaggerated out of all proportion. Try to fix a definite time at this stage rather than make a provisional one that could be extended many times during the withdrawal process. Otherwise there is the danger that you will never actually stop taking the tranquillisers.

How do you want to reduce your dosage?

Once you have decided how long the withdrawal programme will take it is fairly easy to work out how the tablets should be reduced. The most logical method involves a steady reduction, continuing at the same rate until no tablets are being taken. As we have seen in the previous chapter, however, this may not be the best method as people vary in their symptoms from day to day and from week to week.

Decide at this stage whether you would like to reduce on a daily, weekly or monthly basis. This needs some explanation:

- Those who regard the daily dose as the most important like to reduce their daily consumption in fixed amounts. So, for example, after taking 3 tablets daily for a specified time they reduce to 2½ or 2 tablets daily for a similar interval. This is a simple method but does involve sudden changes in reduction. However, there is a big psychological lift from reducing by as much as one tablet a day and holding to this.

- Those who reduce on a weekly basis set a target of the maximum number of tablets that they have to take in a given week and reduce the maximum with each succeeding week. Thus, for example, 34 tablets can be taken in week one and in the following week this can be reduced to 32; 16 weeks later withdrawal will be complete. This technique allows for variation in the intensity of symptoms during the week but does not give an obvious reward at the end of each day.

- Reducing on a monthly basis leads to even more gradual withdrawal. A number of tablets is set aside to be taken over the coming month and it is up to you how you distribute these week by week. This is not a particularly popular method, as some people find it very difficult to hold to the dosage allowed and run out long before the month is up. However, if you are strong-willed this might be the method for you as it allows the most flexibility in varying the dose according to the severity or otherwise of the withdrawal symptoms and ultimately leads to the smoothest withdrawal.

When should each reduction be made?

This may seem another silly question. The most obvious form of reduction is to follow the calendar as in the rapid withdrawal programme, so that after each week you move on to the next stage. The advantage of this is that you can follow your progress easily and predict exactly when you will stop tablets altogether.

Many people dislike being slaves to the calendar, however, and prefer to choose some other yardstick. For example, you may realize that for a few days each month you feel much better than at any other time but this is not always predictable. You may therefore prefer to make your main reductions on these 'good' days, provided you can cope with such an unpredictable fluctuation.

Some people are much more concerned when they have withdrawal symptoms on their own and prefer to have members of their family around them. This is not always possible but if one knows that for the next few days various members of the family *will* be at home then this might be a good time to make the next reduction in your dosage.

So, as these various considerations show, although the calendar may seem the obvious influence controlling the time of reduction it cannot always be assumed to be the best.

How many doses per day?

We noted earlier that every time you take a tablet it has a psychological effect that is quite independent of its chemical effects on the body. Consequently, many people find it difficult to change from 1 tablet four times a day to 2 tablets twice a day. The total dose is the same and the levels of the drug in the body do not change much between doses but the psychological effect of taking the tablets four times a day is quite considerable.

It is possible to take advantage of this when constructing your withdrawal programme. For example (unlike the one dose a day people) when reducing from 2 tablets daily you can change from one tablet twice a day to ½ a tablet three times a day. The reduction will not seem so great if you do it this way. But eventually you will have to cut down the frequency again so, if at all possible, it is best to get down to one dose a day as early as practicable in the withdrawal programme.

Are family and friends on your side?

This may seem yet another silly question. Of course everyone wants you to stop taking your tablets and are prepared to give you as much help as necessary. But before you dismiss this question as completely outrageous just consider whether it is really true. How many times in the past have you been advised to 'take one of your pills' after a family argument or when you are more irritable than usual. Is your partner prepared to put up with you lying awake all night during withdrawal and disturbing his or her sleep as well? If relationships are a bit tense at home even before you start withdrawing can they stand the test of more problems as you reduce?

There is another side to this question as well. When you have been taking tablets for many years you may be regarded as someone who is physically fit but mentally crippled. Other members of the family may come to treat you accordingly. The change is a subtle one; you and they may not even have noticed it. But if you now stop all your tablets it will be difficult for the family to maintain this image of you as an invalid. You will have lifted up your bed and walked. Are the family prepared for this? Can they adjust to the new independent you? Certainly, you ought to ask yourself these questions before you start on your withdrawal programme but, whatever your conclusions, it is in your own and their best interests – long term – to establish that independence.

How much back-sliding is allowed?

Include in your programme a contingency procedure you can follow if you fail to reduce as planned – try to establish rules that you know you *can* follow. Your doctor or another professional such as a health visitor could help here. Don't become bogged down by agonizing over questions such as how many times are you allowed to fail before you give up the programme? If you cannot reduce at the specified time should you give up and start at the beginning or suspend reduction and start again at that point? If so, what is the maximum length of time the programme can be suspended before you start again? In general it is unwise to have more than three attempts to withdraw at any one time and to allow no more than four weeks suspension of the programme.

There is a temptation, too, not to plan for such contingencies because you do not like to contemplate the idea of failure or because you would like to wait and see how you feel if it does come to that. This is not the right approach. You have probably tried it before when reducing your tranquillisers and it has not worked. You need rules to maintain your determination as you go through reduction. Otherwise, there is a possibility that you will never withdraw completely.

51

Date: Total score:

	no symptoms	mild symptoms	moderate symptoms	severe symptoms	intolerable symptoms
	0	1	2	3	4
Monday					
	0	1	2	3	4
Tuesday					
	0	1	2	3	4
Wednesday					
	0	1	2	3	4
Thursday					
	0	1	2	3	4
Friday					
	0	1	2	3	4
Saturday					
	0	1	2	3	4
Sunday					

Instructions: circle the number that comes nearest to your feelings over the last 24 hours.

Figure 2   Chart for recording withdrawal symptoms over each week

Some homework before reduction

Before you finalize your withdrawal programme it may be useful to record how you feel on your present dose of tablets and how much your symptoms vary from day to day. For this purpose the chart (Figure 2) can be used. Make several copies of this and record your feelings for between one and four weeks before starting on your reducing programme. For this purpose, take all your symptoms together – unless you have only one particular withdrawal symptom that concerns you.

As a separate exercise you may wish to find out at which time of day your symptoms are most severe. You may feel you know this already but, again, check it out and record your symptoms each day, using the chart shown in Figure 3.

Date:

	no symptoms	mild symptoms	moderate symptoms	severe symptoms	intolerable symptoms
9–12am	0	1	2	3	4
12–3pm	0	1	2	3	4
3–6pm	0	1	2	3	4
6–9pm	0	1	2	3	4
9–12pm	0	1	2	3	4

Instructions: circle the number that comes nearest to your feelings over each time period.

Figure 3 Chart for recording withdrawal symptoms at different times of day

This should help you to establish whether you are a morning shaker, an evening twitcher or just have the mid-day blues. Knowing how your symptoms change during the day is very relevant to deciding when you ought to take your tablets to produce the maximum effect.

Add up your total score for each week that you have recorded your symptoms, using Figure 2:

- If your score is greater than 18 or you have at least four days on which your score for symptoms is three or above, it is unlikely that you will be able to withdraw successfully at this stage. You have to be prepared for up to a 50 per cent increase in your total symptoms at some time during withdrawal and if your 'baseline' is already high an increase of this degree is likely to be intolerable.
- If your score is less than three you are ready to start withdrawing.

- If you are not quite confident about your withdrawal programme despite a low score, you may like to practise first, as
  described below.

The trial run

A trial run will help you to decide whether your theoretical
reduction programme is appropriate or whether you ought to
modify it.

- For example, you could allow yourself to take extra tablets on
  days when you have to go into a busy shopping centre and
  reduce the dose again on days you are staying at home.
- Similarly, if you suffer from premenstrual tension it may be
  appropriate to increase your dose in the week before your
  menstrual period and reduce it again subsequently. You may
  take most of your tablets in the morning or evening depending
  on how your symptoms change during the course of the day.
  Try to anticipate the times when you have more severe
  symptoms and take your allowed medication between one and
  two hours *before* you expect the symptoms to be in their peak.

Once you start your programme make sure you stick to its
rules because once you deviate from them you are unlikely to
complete the programme successfully. Like a train that has gone
off the rails you will find it exceptionally difficult to get back on
the right track again.

Getting near the end

Many people have a major problem in stopping the last few
tablets in their withdrawal regime. Often by this stage the dose
taken is so small it has no significant chemical effect but the ritual
of taking a pill is like a magic talisman that will ward off evil and
prevent nasty reactions. It is almost like breaking off a relationship with someone who you have never liked very much but has
nonetheless been good to you over the years.

You *can* break through this barrier and it may be helpful to continue scoring your weekly chart. This should convince you that you are still making progress and can maintain this even when you stop all your tablets. Be careful at this stage not to substitute your tranquilliser with other drugs that are more dangerous – particularly tobacco and alcohol. It is understandable that you might slightly increase your normal smoking consumption during the withdrawal phase but be careful to monitor this so that it is reduced later.

If you feel confident of your success you may even plan to give up smoking as well (but not normally at the same time as you are withdrawing from tranquillisers). There are various ways of doing this but the most effective is a substitution of tobacco in cigarettes by nicotine in the form of chewing gum (Nicorette), which can be obtained by private prescription. In reducing your tobacco intake you may adopt exactly the same procedure that you have used in coming off your tranquillisers.

Once you have stopped your tablets completely it is a good insurance policy to carry a few tablets round with you at all times. This will reassure you that there is something to take in an emergency and, because of this, you will probably not need to take anything. It is *not* a sign of weakness to do this. It is like taking out an insurance policy with a very low premium. Once you have completed six months entirely free of tablets you may no longer need to take this precaution.

Even after you have stopped the last tablet and there is no more drug in your system you will still not be completely free from the effects of the drug. This is because the long period for which you have taken the drug will have led to your normal coping reflexes becoming sluggish and disused. You will be able to learn them all over again but this will take several months and you may therefore continue to suffer more symptoms than you expected – although these should not be as bad as the acute withdrawal problems. What is most important is that you understand what is happening at this stage and do not give up feeling that you will have to start taking tranquillisers again regularly.

In emergencies you can still take a tablet occasionally because, as we have seen earlier, this is perfectly safe and does *not* mean that you are back on the road to addiction. After you have stopped tranquillisers altogether, obviously, it is wise to avoid regular consumption again – but it would be ridiculous to rely on tobacco or alcohol to relieve distress in the future if an occasional tranquilliser could be taken instead. If you can avoid them, so much the better, but it is not a sign of failure or relapse to have one occasionally at times of crisis.

6

Other Ways of Stopping
Tranquillisers

All the suggestions made so far have been concerned with strategies of reduction. The aim has been to deceive your body, and particularly your central nervous system, so that the removal of tranquillisers from your system passes unnoticed and there are no withdrawal reactions. In this chapter I am assuming that all your withdrawal strategies have failed and you need additional treatment over the withdrawal period. These treatments can be psychological, many of which you can try yourself without any professional help; or they can be medical, and will therefore need the help of your doctor. These are no substitute for a strategy of withdrawal; they are just additional aids. In using them you will still need to follow one of the withdrawal programmes outlined in earlier chapters.

Psychological treatments

Coping with panic

Panic is a common problem during withdrawal from tranquillisers. For no apparent reason, and without the slightest warning, you get an overwhelming feeling of terror and fear of some unknown threat. This is associated with severe physical symptoms, sometimes only one or two, sometimes many. These include:

- Tightness in the chest with difficulty in breathing
- Palpitations and feeling of your heart beating very fast
- Flushing
- Sweating
- Feeling dizzy and lightheaded
- Uncontrollable shaking.

These may be followed by tingling in the fingers and toes and muscle twitching.

Because the physical symptoms are present at the same time as the mental ones the panic attack is sometimes thought to be a physical condition. The most common fear is that you are developing a heart attack and, because the feelings are so terrible, the thought can easily cross your mind that you are dying. You may also fear that the panic attack is the gateway to madness, and before long you will pass through and be lost to the world of normal mental life.

Although such attacks last for only a short time, seldom longer than an hour, they influence every part of life. Because they are completely unpredictable you tend to withdraw to places which you consider as 'safe', so that if you have a panic attack at least you are in familiar surroundings and are unlikely to make a fool of yourself. This can lead to the development of phobias, so that you avoid going out to shops and public places because of the fear of an attack.

Unfortunately, phobias can become fixed even if you develop no further panic attacks. You may be so frightened of having another panic that many places become 'out of bounds'. The continued avoidance of these places only makes the phobia worse. You can develop agoraphobia that is so severe that you never go out of the house. This is far worse than being dependent on tranquillisers yet being able to travel anywhere.

It is therefore essential to come to terms with panic and thus prevent it from taking over your life. This involves having some knowledge of how the body reacts to stress and exactly what happens during a panic attack.

How the body reacts to stress

When you feel anxious your brain reacts by making more hormones, particularly adrenaline, and by stimulating nervous pathways to the muscles, stomach, bowel, bladder, heart and sweat glands. Most of these pathways are outside conscious control and form what is called the autonomic nervous system.

These changes allow you to run faster, be more powerful and aggressive, react more quickly and be more alert. They aid self-preservation when you are being attacked by a mugger or trying to escape from a natural disaster such as an earthquake.

In a panic attack, these valuable reactions are massively stimulated all at once and at the wrong time – when there is no obvious threat. Your heart beats like a kettledrum, your muscles tense up for action, you shake in anticipation, the sweat pours off you and you are sensitive to the slightest danger. But no danger can be seen. You wait on tenterhooks to escape from a situation you cannot understand. Instead of your body carrying out your commands it seems to be reacting on its own and trying to control you.

The bodily and mental changes in a panic attack are the same as healthy responses to stress, except that they take place in the absence of obvious threat and are much more intense. There is no real evidence that an attack of panic does any harm and the fears of death or of passing out, although understandable, are not justified. Once you can convince yourself of this you can take panic outside the realms of physical illness and dismiss any comparisons with heart attacks, strokes or epileptic fits. Say to yourself when you have the symptoms of panic, 'this is a mental reaction and has a mental cause'. Otherwise you may be tempted to seek referral to a medical specialist.

Once you have persuaded your doctor to make such a referral your thoughts will then go along medical tramlines. You judge that the doctor would not have made the referral unless he felt that you possibly had a medical illness. By the time you see the specialist you will probably have convinced yourself that it does have a medical cause, probably a serious one. If the doctor finds nothing on examination and tells you that there is nothing to worry about you will not be reassured. You are likely to demand 'proper investigations' and have blood tests, cardiographs and special x-rays. When these turn out to be normal you may miserably convince yourself that the doctors are incompetent and have not done the right tests. Before long you have seen a string of specialists, too, all of whom have given you different advice, and you finish up more confused then ever.

It is right to consider medical causes for any symptoms but if they are the same as those described in a typical panic attack it is much more reasonable to treat them as such if that is your doctor's diagnosis. Yet again we come round to the central point of taking some personal responsibility for dealing with your symptoms and the problem of tranquilliser withdrawal.

Some simple strategies

Whatever the cause of your panic, the following simple strategies will help you to overcome the feelings or at least get them into more reasonable proportion.

- If you start to get feelings that make you think you are going to have a panic attack, first reassure yourself that there is *no real danger* of you collapsing or having a major physical illness.
- Also, tell yourself that even if you have these feelings they will not automatically progress to a full panic attack. In short, do not let your thoughts run away with you and expect the worst to happen.
- It will help too, if you can concentrate your attention instead on breathing as deeply and rhythmically as possible; this has a very soothing effect.

If, despite these new attitudes, you still find the symptoms getting worse, there are several things that you could do. The immediate reaction is to run away. This is a natural feeling that we all get when faced by something extremely frightening but in a panic attack it is the *wrong* thing to do; running away will only reinforce the idea that the place where you had the panic attack is a dangerous one. This will lead to a phobia about that place and you will avoid it. If you have panic attacks in dozens of different places you can become afraid to go out of the house at all and develop severe agoraphobia. So, it is much better to stay than to run. Severe panic cannot last for very long because your body is unable to remain on 'emergency stations' for longer than about half an hour. Tell yourself: whatever happens, and no matter where you are, you will become less anxious before long.

If you do stay in the same place, you will start to feel better and can then continue what you were doing before you had the panic attack. Now, if your attack occurs when you are in a busy street you may feel that it is difficult to stay there without attracting attention. However, I can assure you that most of the people around you will not have recognized that you are distressed in any way. People tend to go about their daily business without paying too much attention to complete strangers and the common feeling that everyone is staring at you is almost certainly mistaken. It will help you to calm these feelings if you carry out a perfectly natural manoeuvre – such as reading a newspaper, looking in your bag, gazing at shop windows or sitting down on the nearest bench. Whatever technique you use, take it slowly and smoothly. If you do this no one will be able to detect that there is anything wrong with you. And when the panic feelings begin to subside you can give yourself a pat on the back . . . you have achieved a very important victory. It will reassure you that there is nothing to be afraid of and your confidence will return. Once this starts to happen, wait until you are ready and then continue the activity or task that you had set yourself before the panic attack began.

If you adopt this strategy you should be able to overcome most panics. And once you have mastered your attacks of panic you will find eventually that they no longer take place. It is as though you were fighting an enemy who knows that now you have superior weapons and decides to surrender. It is common for the panic attacks to get less severe and less frequent although they may not disappear altogether for some time. If you go for several weeks without a panic attack and then get another one don't feel demoralized. Instead, congratulate yourself on the number of attacks you have prevented by dealing more constructively with your feelings. Tell yourself, too, that these occasional break-throughs will become less and less frequent.

Panic attacks were named after the god Pan in ancient Greece. He was a mythical half man, half animal who enjoyed frightening unwary travellers by jumping out in front of them on lonely forest paths when they were returning home. He took great delight in their cries of alarm and was even more gleeful if they ran away screaming but, in fact, he was quite harmless and the travellers who stayed their ground came to no harm. Remember this when Pan visits you again!

Relaxation and hypnosis

All the symptoms of tranquilliser withdrawal are associated with a high level of anxiety and if you are able to relax many of these withdrawal symptoms will improve and perhaps disappear altogether. The problem here, of course, is that it is easy to ask people to relax but much more difficult for the anxious person to carry out a relaxation programme. Paradoxically, we can all relax best when we least need to and when we are at our most anxious the ability seems to leave us. For this reason, the aim of relaxation training is to learn techniques that can be brought into use whenever anxiety and withdrawal symptoms begin to trouble you.

Almost everyone has heard about relaxation training and there are many books and self-help groups that concentrate on teaching these skills, which can include yoga exercises and meditation techniques. All of these can help us to detach our minds from the worries about us and allow our bodies to relax in a natural way. This leads to beneficial changes in the blood flow in different organs, a reduction in blood pressure and heart rate, less sweating and slower, deeper breathing.

These changes may all help you to control your symptoms of tranquilliser withdrawal, both direct symptoms such as palpitations and shaking, and indirect ones such as a sense of unreality, excessive sensitivity to noise and light, and dizziness. Any means of reducing these symptoms is worth trying.

Full relaxation training tends to be carried out in a comfortable armchair in a quiet room and it is impossible to recreate these conditions when, for example, you are out shopping. Nevertheless, once you have developed a knack of 'switching off' your mind, relaxation can be used anywhere.

If you doubt this, try the following exercise the next time you notice a withdrawal symptom coming on. This may be one you have had many times in the past but is much worse during withdrawal or it could be a completely new symptom. To make it more difficult we shall assume that the symptom comes on when you are pushing a trolley round a supermarket. Obviously, you cannot there and then lie down on the floor and start your relaxation programme. You must do it in a quieter way, by concentrating on the way you are breathing:

Take much slower and deeper breaths, making sure that you get the air deep down into the lungs instead of just at the top of the chest.

As you do this you will find that your arms and hands relax so that the whites of your knuckles no longer show as you grip the supermarket trolley.

Do not move on until you feel the tension flowing out of your hands. With each deep breath you should feel your tension flowing away and, as it does, your withdrawal symptom goes also.

Under these circumstances withdrawal symptoms seldom disappear but even a small reduction in their severity will boost your confidence. You have shown that they can be brought under your control to some extent and if you work on this technique you may be able to conquer the symptoms altogether. It is best to practise at home when you are feeling at your most settled but you can try out these techniques wherever and almost whenever you wish. Obviously, it would be dangerous to practise them while driving a car or supervising delicate machinery. The ultimate aim is to be able to relax when you need to and to concentrate at other times. It is a bonus factor that, once you have learned to relax, you will find your concentration also improves markedly.

Hypnosis can also be used as an aid to relaxation and it is not nearly as complicated as many people believe. Unfortunately many people also look on it as a way of overcoming a problem without much in the way of personal effort. It is nice to entertain fantasies of being put to sleep and being cured by the magic of hypnosis, but it is not that simple. Some people are good hypnotic subjects and others are extremely poor. Unfortunately, anxious people who are more prone to dependence tend also to be poor hypnotic subjects and often need many sessions before they can enter even a moderate trance. In general, therefore, hypnosis is not usually a good treatment for tranquilliser dependence but its close cousin, auto-hypnosis (self-hypnosis), may be a useful aid to relaxation and to 'switching off' withdrawal symptoms when they cause stress.

For example, let us see how auto-hypnosis might help a withdrawal symptom such as twitching of the muscles. We shall assume that you have had this symptom throughout the day and have just come home in the evening. You are extremely tense and your twitching muscles are driving you mad. Sit in a comfortable chair and try the following technique. You can either say the words out loud or silently repeat them to yourself. However, it is not sufficient just to read the instructions without practising them. You must say the words in your head:

'I am concentrating on the twitching in my muscles, all over my body, and as I concentrate I find I become more aware of these twitchings and the tension in all the muscles.
The more I concentrate on the tension and the twitching, the more I feel the tension being changed by relaxation.
The muscles are no longer tense and taut; they are relaxing and becoming heavier and more comfortable. As my muscles become more comfortable and relaxed the twitching goes.
My mind feels more relaxed. I can think of quiet things – a white swan serene on the water, a favourite photograph or picture, a vase of flowers – and feel gradually more settled as my worries and tension drain away.
Now I am feeling completely relaxed and settled. I will remember this feeling when I need to in the future. When I say the number 42 in my mind I will remember this relaxing feeling and all my muscles will slowly become relaxed and settled again and all the twitching feelings will go.'

Now count gradually from 42 to 50. With each succeeding

number you will feel more awake and when you get to 50 you can continue your normal activities.

If you have been able to concentrate on the words you will find that your muscle tension *has* reduced. The trouble is that when people feel at their most nervous they concentrate less well and it may therefore be necessary for you to repeat the words over and over before your concentration becomes good enough to receive the message of auto-hypnosis. The number '42' is given as what is technically called 'a post-hypnotic suggestion'. If you practise this technique over and over again, you will come to associate the number with feelings of relaxation and whenever you concentrate on the number you will be able to relax again.

This is only a short outline of hypnotic techniques and the interested reader may like to increase their knowledge by consulting other books on the theory and practice of hypnotism. These books are unlikely to include discussion of the use of hypnosis in treating tranquilliser withdrawal but, as we have seen with so many other treatments, there is a great overlap between withdrawal symptoms and those of tension and anxiety. A more detailed account of anxiety control training can be found in Dr Philip Snaith's book mentioned in the Appendix.

Making sense of your symptoms

Throughout this book we have assumed that symptoms after stopping tranquillisers are outside your control because they are caused by chemical dependence. Some of these symptoms you may have had before starting tranquillisers, but not to the same degree, and others may be completely new. It is therefore reasonable to suppose that these feelings would not have occurred if you had never taken tranquillisers. You are therefore fighting a battle against alien feelings that are forcing you to go on taking tablets that you do not want.

But there is another way of tackling your symptoms. You can accept them as part of your normal experiences and try to come to terms with them. The more you know about them the less unusual they will seem and before long they will be accepted simply as odd feelings that you get from time to time. You may even come to appreciate them as giving you an extra dimension to your appreciation of life that others lack.

This suggestion may shock you. After all, no one wants to have terrible feelings of panic, unreality or odd bodily sensations, so how can they be regarded as positive qualities? A comparison with physical illness may help you to understand. Some people are born with a minor physical handicap, say, large ears. When young they suffer greatly because of the unerring ability of children to notice the slightest deviation from normal and make it a subject for ridicule. So cries of 'bat's ears' and 'elephant-ears' follow children with large ears round the school playground and it is hardly surprising that many become very self-conscious and inquire about the possibility of plastic surgery to correct the deformity. Others adjust to the apparent handicap and may even find some advantage in it. After all, our ears do to some extent act as a funnel to channel sound waves into the ear. Large ears are usually better funnels than small ears and so may be better at picking up sound waves.

We now have two groups of big-eared people. One suffers greatly, is acutely self-conscious and exaggerates the handicap so that it affects all parts of life. The other accepts the abnormality not only as a fact of life but as a possible advantage and, by so doing, it ceases to be a handicap, if it ever was one.

The same attitudes can apply to symptoms of tranquilliser dependence. Most people see them as unwelcome visitations that have nothing to do with normal emotional life, but some can adjust to them and even derive some slight advantage from their presence. For example, hypersensitivity to noise, smell, sight and touch are important symptoms of tranquilliser withdrawal, although many are also found in people who are generally anxious. Although this can be irritating it also has advantages, as faint sensations can be detected which others would ignore. So the creak of the burglar forcing open the window, the smell of gas from the unlit cooker, and the flicker of the lamp that has an unsafe electrical connection will all be detected more easily by those going through withdrawal reactions after stopping tranquillisers.

The bonus of a positive attitude towards such heightened awareness is that once a symptom is accepted, or even prized, it is no longer a worry. Instead of invading your consciousness like a bat out of hell it is more like a harmless cat – playing little direct part in your life but sometimes reassuring by being around.

In this 'positive' respect let us take a closer look at the symptom of unreality. This particular withdrawal symptom causes a great deal of unnecessary worry. When it is first experienced people understandably fear they are going mad, as a feeling from being cut off from the experience of your self (depersonalization) or the world around you (derealization) is very disturbing – as you may appreciate from personal experience. There is a fear that you will retreat even further from the real world like a capsule launched into space, and will no longer be able to trust your senses. In fact, the feelings of unreality have nothing to do with madness and do not in themselves do any harm. In some ways they are protective, as the reactions of your body to stress – palpitations, sweating, muscle tension, difficulty in breathing – are all reduced when you feel unreal and so your body functions at a slower rate.

The main disadvantage of regarding withdrawal symptoms as due entirely to the drugs you have been taking for so long is the tendency to sit back and be virtuous. 'Look at the terrible symptoms,' you may cry, 'all caused by these drugs. The doctor never told me they were addictive, they should never have been prescribed.' This attitude does not help anybody, least of all you. Instead, you could ask the doctor whom you regard as responsible to give you another treatment to help you to come off your tranquillisers.

The worst you can do is to regard yourself as hopelessly addicted for life because of a medical mistake. If you adopt this frame of mind, you may regard every new symptom as due to chemical dependence on tranquillisers. Thus completely unrelated problems such as joint pains, vaginal discharge, skin rashes, migraine, stomach ulcers, constipation, ear trouble (such as Ménières Disease), deteriorating eyesight and heart trouble have all been blamed on tranquilliser dependence.

A little honesty will tell you this is nonsense. You sought advice from your doctor in the first place because of nervous symptoms, most of which are probably similar in many respects to your present ones. The medical profession is far from blameless as it should have detected tranquilliser dependence earlier, with benzodiazepines in particular, but it is likely that the doctor who first prescribed your tranquillisers had little or no idea of this risk at that time. Indeed, if you have been taking tranquillisers for more than seven years it is almost certain that you were prescribed your tranquillisers in all good faith as a safe alternative to the barbiturates and other similar drugs, to help you avoid the risks of dependence with these older compounds.

And when you started taking the tranquillisers you were not hooked immediately. You went back for more tablets because they were helping you; they were not forced on you by the doctor. Obviously, if you had known the risks of dependence at that time you might not have been so keen to continue taking these drugs and may well have stopped taking them while you still could do so reasonably easily, but it would be wrong to conclude that you had no part to play in the development of your dependence.

Review and record

You do need to take some responsibility for the process of breaking your addiction. This can include a review of your apparent withdrawal and dependent symptoms to see how many of them can be brought under your control and whether they are really true withdrawal problems. It does not matter if you are too generous in this exercise, and include symptoms that are caused entirely by dependence, as even these can be modulated by your attitudes and determination.

List all your withdrawal symptoms, separating those that you think are definitely caused by stopping your drugs and those that might be caused by drug withdrawal but could have other explanations. Then make sufficient copies of Figure 4 on p. 69 to cover the number of weeks you wish to continue assessing your

Time	Monday	Tuesday	Wednesday	Thursday	Friday	Saturday	Sunday
9–12am activity symptom							
3–6pm activity symptom							
6–9pm activity symptom							
9–12pm activity symptom							

Figure 4 Linking your symptoms and activities

symptoms, and the symptoms you wish to record. If you need more space to record your activities each day as well as your symptoms, construct a larger chart; it is better to record too much than too little.

Now keep a record of your symptoms and activities. You can continue this for as long as you wish before starting on your withdrawal programme, or you might introduce a small token reduction in your drug dosage to find out if it has any effect. The point of this exercise is to establish links between what you are doing and thinking and your symptoms. It would help if you do not assume in advance that all your feelings are directly due to chemical dependence and are therefore withdrawal symptoms. Many, you will find, are more closely related to your thoughts and actions.

By the end of this trial recording period, particularly if it includes reduction of dosage, you should be able to divide your symptoms into three groups:

- The first consists of symptoms that are related entirely to your drug consumption and are likely to be true withdrawal effects.
- The second are related directly to your thinking and activities.
- The third consists of symptoms that are completely un-predictable and make no sort of sense.

Let us look at examples of each group:

- If your muscles get tense and twitchy every evening at about nine o'clock just before you take your only tablet of the day, and if these symptoms are much worse when you reduce your dose to half a tablet, it is reasonable to conclude that your muscle twitching is a genuine withdrawal symptom.
- If, on the other hand, you get palpitations several times a day only when you are meeting your colleagues at work this symptom falls into the second group.
- If you have panics from between one and ten times a week at completely unpredictable times, this would fall into the third group. (I hope that before long you will find that the symptoms in this third group become fewer as you begin to

70

understand them and link them to other things that are going on in your life.)

Try not to have fixed ideas about your symptoms before you start filling in your forms. If you do not carry out this exercise with an open mind you might as well not start at all, because you will fill in the forms without thinking and just confirm your prejudices.

It is often more difficult to record your thoughts than your activities at the end of each day but they, too, may be very important in triggering your symptoms. You may say, for instance, that a panic attack came out of the blue, but just try to recall what you were thinking about before you had the panic. You may have realized that you were far from home and that none of your friends or relatives knew where you were, or that the crowded room in which you are sitting reminds you of the last time you had a panic attack in a busy supermarket. If in doubt, write down the thoughts you had just before the symptoms started, on a form like that shown in Figure 5.

Date	Symptom	Time of onset	Thoughts before symptoms began	Thoughts after symptoms began

Figure 5   Record of thoughts before and after withdrawal symptoms

Filling in the form will help you to identify the unhelpful thoughts that may trigger off your symptoms. It will also show you how constructive thinking can stop the symptom from developing further, or even remove it altogether. For instance, if you feel just a little light-headed when in a busy street your past experiences may lead you along the tramline thoughts of panic. You develop more symptoms – sweating, trembling, tightness in the chest – and become convinced you are going to pass out. By thinking like this you are three-quarters of the way to fulfilling your fears. In other words, you have a panic simply because you expect to have one.

A more constructive line of thinking would be to relate your dizziness to the heat of the day or the fact that you have not eaten anything since breakfast. You therefore get into the shade or have a snack in the nearest restaurant.

Thoughts and actions cannot be separated completely but, as you can see from the example just given, it is the thoughts that come first and they are often more important.

Once you have sorted out your symptoms in this way they will no longer be so frightening; they can be predicted and they can be cut down to size. When you re-start your withdrawal programme in earnest you will then find that you can deal with any new symptoms in the same way as your more familiar ones. You can also reassure yourself that, whatever these new symptoms are like, they will not last long and will be over for good soon after you stop taking tranquillisers entirely.

Continue recording your thoughts, activities and symptoms until you have confidence in predicting your feelings and responding to them. You will know when it is time to stop filling in the forms because you will feel bored because the forms have nothing more to tell you and secure because you are back in control of your life again. It is rather like learning to drive a car. To begin with every part of driving is a strain but as you increase in confidence the driving instructor becomes more and more of a nuisance and finally you can dispense with him altogether.

After the withdrawal

'Post-withdrawal blues' can be a serious problem because it comes on at a time when you are not expecting trouble. You have been through the nasty experiences following reduction of your tablets and it is natural to feel a sense of triumph when you stop your tablets completely. If you then continue to get symptoms it is easy to get demoralized and to think it was a waste of time ever going through the process of withdrawal.

The symptoms you get in the post-withdrawal period are not usually as bad as those during withdrawal but because you cannot connect them to reducing your tablets they can seem worse. For example, if you go through a period of unreality soon after stopping your drugs you may wrongly come to the conclusion that it is permanent and can only be solved by going back on your tranquilliser again. Do not despair at this critical stage. We have already mentioned that it takes time for your nervous system to adjust to coming off tranquillisers and that the protective mechanisms that help to keep you going against life's pressures fall into disrepair when you are on these drugs. You need time to learn how to cope again, and with the new resources you have picked up during withdrawal from tranquillisers you should be able to overcome these without too much difficulty. It will need patience and stamina, not pessimism and doubt.

We still do not know enough about withdrawal problems to understand why some people experience post-withdrawal blues while others do not. Whatever happens, do not assume that you are bound to have difficulties in the post-withdrawal period just because you had trouble in getting off tranquillisers. For some people there is a dramatic improvement within as little as three weeks of stopping their drugs, when life really becomes alive and is not a drug-dominated drudge. This goal can be attained by all but some will take longer to achieve it than others.

Self help groups

Many people who are dependent on tranquillisers go through a stage when they feel that no one else really understands their symptoms. They may have been told that all their symptoms are either imaginary or grossly exaggerated and that all can be solved by 'pulling yourself together'. This phrase occurs time and time again in the field of mental health and it is almost always inappropriate. The very phrase itself is odd; you tend to pull yourself apart, not together.

At times such as these it is important to be able to talk to people who do understand what you are going through. Self help groups offer a sympathetic and understanding voice to people in distress and tranquilliser dependence is no exception. Groups have been set up in many countries. Some groups are linked to similar groups dealing with drug dependence with heroin, cocaine and other more severe drugs of addiction. But in most cases they are kept apart. People who are dependent on tranquillisers have little in common with typical drug abusers.

In the United Kingdom a separate branch of the self help organization for drug abusers, Release, has been set up for people who are dependent on tranquillisers. This is called Tranx Release and there are branches in many parts of the country. Some are given in the Appendix but as they are springing up so rapidly you are quite likely to find others that are nearer your home than one of the groups listed. Your local Citizens' Advice Bureau or public library will probably have information about the nearest group.

In the United States most of these organisations are still linked with those for drug dependence. Information about the 3600 drug-abuse treatment centres in the United States (and its territories) is available from the National Clearinghouse for Drug Abuse Information. The address is given in the Appendix.

Most people contact their self help group by telephone in the first instance. Do not be put off if you find you are connected to an answerphone. So many calls come through to these groups that answerphones are often necessary to keep track of all the calls. Before long, however, you should be able to speak to the organizer of the group. In virtually every case the local organizer will be a person who has been (or still is) dependent on tranquillisers. You will therefore speak to someone who knows the problem from the inside and will not give you easy answers or dismiss your difficulties as hysterical or neurotic. This first contact can be a great relief because it allows sharing of the problem, and the pain.

Many people are happy to continue contact by telephone only, asking for advice and support when needed, but not meeting others in a group. Others may occasionally attend meetings and a few, somewhere between 10 and 20 per cent of the total, will take part in regular group meetings.

The objectives of these groups vary. Although many are primarily concerned with withdrawal from tranquillisers, many more have wider aims. These include improving confidence, self-esteem and assertiveness, and improving awareness of the problems that originally caused people to take tranquillisers. For many who appear to have chronic tension and anxiety the financial, housing and personal problems that cause the anxiety never change and so the anxiety appears to be part of the person's functioning. By improving awareness of these issues possible solutions can be explored and followed through. If the long term stresses can be resolved, this may allow successful tranquilliser withdrawal to take place, too.

Your local self help groups can also be a valuable mine of information about new methods of treatment, workshops on subjects related to tranquilliser dependence, and information such as lists of sympathetic general practitioners and other Health Authority personnel. Some people only seem to need the occasional phone call, others attend for years. If you feel you are getting stuck and have nowhere else to turn please think of your local self help group before giving up.

Groups normally meet once a week and sometimes relatives are invited also. Because many more women than men suffer from tranquilliser dependence the group programme may be for women only. However, all sufferers should be able to find a group within a reasonable distance that can meet their needs.

From this you will see that people vary in their wishes and needs and not all enjoy the prospect of talking about their symptoms in groups. Some are too shy and inhibited to talk freely and can only contemplate withdrawal on their own, possibly with the aid of telephone support. Others prefer the mutual support provided by a group and make much more progress through regular meetings, often at weekly intervals. Of course, a great deal depends on the other members of the group. If you respect and sympathize with them you are more likely to talk freely and accept their advice and support. One bad experience with a group does not mean that all groups are wrong for you.

Virtually all self help groups for tranquilliser dependence are self financing and very few receive support from organizations such as local authorities. Some are able to obtain funds from charities but these amounts are usually very small. Remember this when, for example, making telephone calls. If the local organizer has to make many telephone calls a day the bills can mount up and usually the organizer has to pay. You will appreciate that it is best for the person requesting the advice to make the telephone calls wherever possible.

Medical treatments

Medical treatments should be considered last, even though they are easier to put into practice than many of the other psychological treatments. All cross country runners sometimes wish for a car to pull up and transport them to the finishing line (although they will probably regret it later). Many people who have been dependent on tranquillisers are also reluctant to take other tablets or treatment from doctors even when they are recommended. This is predictable, and in some ways I am surprised not to see this reaction more often, as it would take a great deal to reassure *me* that another tablet was completely safe after many years of chemical dependence.

All medical treatments involve seeing your own doctor first. This can be a major stumbling block. Many people who have been dependent on tranquillisers are not on good terms with their doctors. Those who feel dissatisfied may have been told to reduce their tablets using their own will-power or casually dismissed with a comment that there is no problem with taking tranquillisers and they might as well continue on them indefinitely.

These impressions of dismissal may be correct but often they are exaggerated. It is worth reminding yourself that family doctors are all-purpose practitioners who have to be competent in all branches of medicine. This is true even for those parts of the subject that do not really interest them. So all general practitioners cannot be expected to be right up to date with tranquilliser dependence. Even now, not a great deal is known about the management of tranquilliser dependence, and most of what is known has been compressed into the last few years.

There is a lot of debate in the medical profession and many doctors are sceptical about the dangers of tranquilliser addiction. In some ways they are right to be, as the subject has been blown up out of all proportion in some quarters. Statements such as 'dependence on benzodiazepines is much worse than dependence on hard drugs' are nonsense, and unnecessarily scare thousands of people. Those who cannot stop their benzodiazepines do have a real dependence problem but this is in quite a different league from addiction to amphetamines, LSD, methadone, cocaine and heroin.

So if your doctor sometimes appears to be unsympathetic to your problem do understand that he is getting conflicting advice from the rest of the medical profession and is not just being difficult or disinterested. It may be possible for you to see another partner from the same practice if you feel a new approach is needed. Many people dependent on tranquillisers feel that younger doctors are more understanding about tranquilliser dependence than older ones but it is dangerous to generalize.

There have also been claims that sexist attitudes sometimes enter into doctors' views about tranquilliser dependence. Obviously, if women are left with the impression that their doctor thinks they only worry about silly things like tranquilliser dependence because they have nothing to do all day, a good doctor-patient relationship is difficult to foster. Another sexist view is that women are naturally dependent and so if they did not have tranquillisers on which to depend they would pick on something else, like lime juice or brazil nuts. I hope you do not come across reactions like this but if you do it is best to seek help elsewhere, preferably from a female doctor in the practice or health centre.

Most doctors, however, are concerned about the large numbers of prescriptions of tranquillisers and would be only too keen for you to stop taking your tablets. A few may be able to help by giving some of the psychological treatments already discussed, such as hypnosis and relaxation therapy. When asked to consider prescribing other tablets to help you stop taking your tranquillisers they have a number of choices: beta-blocking drugs, antidepressants and mild sedatives (but not other addictive) drugs.

Beta-blocking drugs These have already been mentioned in Chapter 1. They are so named because they block some of the effects of adrenaline and similar hormones on the body. These hormones are largely responsible for the bodily changes that are so troublesome in ordinary anxiety and which become terrifying in a panic attack.

The main use of beta-blockers is in the treatment of high blood pressure and other heart disease. In very much lower dosage, however, they are useful in treating anxiety, particularly when symptoms such as palpitations and trembling are marked and cause most concern.

As withdrawal symptoms include such unpleasant bodily feelings as palpitations, sweating and shaking it might be expected that beta-blockers would be helpful in getting people off tranquillisers. In fact, they do have some benefit, but because they only block some of the hormone effects they rarely prevent withdrawal symptoms altogether. Where they score over the other tablets used to help withdrawal symptoms is in having no direct mental effects so it is impossible to become hooked on these drugs and when the time comes to stop taking them there will be no withdrawal symptoms.

Many beta-blocking drugs are available on prescription (and

only on prescription) but the oldest and best known is pro-pranolol. There is no evidence that the newer beta-blocking drugs are superior to this drug in helping withdrawal symptoms.

Antidepressants We have also discussed antidepressants in Chapter 1. Although they are sometimes thought of as tranquillisers they work in quite a different way. They have two groups of effects:

- One is a general sedative effect which is incidental to their main action and can cause problems through drowsiness.
- The other is related to its long-term actions on the brain and is only shown after the drug has been given for several weeks in regular dosage. These long-term effects include the relief of depression and anxiety.

These drugs are quite different from those prescribed for sedation. In fact, they are more related to stimulation than sedation as they improve self-confidence and esteem.

Many people who are dependent on tranquillisers have taken antidepressants in the past because depression is often mixed with anxiety. Indeed, you may be taking them now with your tranquilliser. In the past antidepressants were often combined with tranquillisers in drugs with names like Limbitrol, Triptafen and Motival. You may also know from experience that depression is a common symptom during withdrawal from tranquillisers and will quite understand why they are sometimes given to help over the withdrawal period.

However, the decision to give antidepressants as a treatment for benzodiazepine dependence cannot be made lightly. The antidepressants will have to be given regularly for at least four weeks before you start reducing your benzodiazepine and usually have to be continued until you have stopped your benzodiazepines completely.

Antidepressants can sometimes have side-effects such as dry mouth and constipation and these should not be confused with symptoms of withdrawal. These side-effects vary according to which antidepressant you are taking and can be largely overcome

79

by your doctor prescribing the drug most suitable for your needs.

Lastly, there is just a little concern about difficulties in stopping antidepressants after prolonged dosage. Although there is no evidence of any significant degree of chemical dependence some people find if they stop their antidepressants suddenly they are more nervous over the next few days, and may even have a panic attack or two. This does not happen if the drugs are reduced slowly. It is therefore important not to stop taking antidepressants suddenly. Nine people out of ten do not have any problems, but you may be the tenth.

Other sedative drugs The most obvious type of drug to help you stop taking your tranquillisers is one that has the same effects as the drug you are now taking but which can be stopped without much difficulty. Unfortunately such a drug does not exist. It is a sad fact that the more effective the tranquilliser the more likely it is to be addictive. So, if your doctor changes you to a different drug which appears to be even better than your existing tranquilliser it almost certainly is potentially more addictive.

If you have been taking a benzodiazepine tranquilliser for many years and have tried many times to stop without success it may be appropriate for you to change to another benzodiazepine drug before withdrawal. You will know from Table 1 on page 13 that the dependence risk of benzodiazepines varies considerably, this being mainly related to how long they act in the body. A drug such as triazolam only has tranquillising effects for about four hours but is more addictive than flurazepam which has tranquillising effects for up to 40 hours.

The speed at which the drug is absorbed into the body may also be related to its dependence risk. A drug which is absorbed quickly and gives you a bit of a 'buzz' is more likely to lead to addiction than one that is absorbed slowly.

When you change from one benzodiazepine to another you do not lose the addiction acquired with the first substance. Some degree of addiction will be transferred to the new substance but, if your doctor has chosen the right replacement drug, you will find it easier to withdraw.

Check the drug you are taking with those listed in Table 1 to see whether it is worth asking your doctor to change it for a different benzodiazepine. If you are taking a drug with a 'fairly high' risk of dependence it may be worth changing to the equivalent dose of a drug with a 'moderate' risk. However, not all of the drugs listed in Table 1 are available on prescription in the National Health Service and, if your doctor agrees to the change, a private prescription may be needed.

If a change is agreed you can either start immediately on the new drug or a gradual replacement of one drug with the other over a period of two weeks can be arranged. Because both drugs are of the same class you will not have any severe withdrawal symptoms although there could be a minor increase in some of your anxious symptoms because of a difference in the duration of action between the two drugs. There is also the possibility of developing 'pseudo withdrawal symptoms', if this is the first time for many years that you have stopped taking your original tranquilliser and you therefore expect to have unpleasant reactions. However, I hope by the time you get to this chapter you will be able to recognize which of your symptoms are those of genuine chemical dependence and which are primarily psychological.

If you are taking a benzodiazepine which is listed in Table 1 as having a moderate risk of dependence it may still be appropriate for you to change to another benzodiazepine of moderate risk. This is because people's responses to different substances vary and even a minor improvement could help to make your withdrawal programme succeed. It should be easier to withdraw later, too, because you will have proved to yourself already that the drug you formerly took for many years is not essential to your well-being.

Problems in changing tranquillisers

There is one danger about changing from one benzodiazepine to another, or indeed to any other tranquilliser. Some people are nervous about stopping their original tranquilliser and like to take the new drug in conjunction with the old before making the change. Although this can be carried out over a mere two weeks, as described above, it is important to fix the time of changeover and make it as short as possible. Otherwise there is a danger you will feel nervous about stopping the old drug and continue on two drugs whereas formerly you were only addicted to one. This may seem obvious but I have found it occurs all too often in my clinical practice. Other drugs have been used to help people stop taking tranquillisers but none of them have been investigated sufficiently to allow clear recommendations about their use:

- The so-called 'major tranquillisers' listed in Table 2 have sedative properties and no dependence risk. These work in quite a different way from benzodiazepines and are often useful in treating anxiety because they carry no risk of dependence. It may therefore be thought that these drugs would be ideal in helping to withdraw from benzodiazepines. In fact, the evidence suggests that they either have no value or may even make the symptoms of withdrawal worse.

- The antihistamines, such as promethazine, are safe drugs that have been used in clinical practice for many years. They also have no dependence risk and are alternatives to the benzo-diazepines and other addictive tranquillisers. They may help in aiding withdrawal from benzodiazepines and there is no evidence that they make withdrawal symptoms worse.

- Another drug, chlormethiazole, may also be used. This is not a benzodiazepine but has a significant risk of dependence. It is used frequently for treating the symptoms of withdrawal from alcohol addiction. Because it carries its own risk of depend-ence, its regular use is not recommended. In alcohol with-drawal chlormethiazole is first prescribed in large doses with rapid reduction later so that by the tenth day after withdrawal it is stopped completely. It has not been tested in the treatment of benzodiazepine withdrawal.

Because gradual reduction of drugs during benzodiazepine withdrawal is recommended regular treatment is likely to be necessary over a much longer period than ten days. There is therefore a real danger that dependence to chlormethiazole could develop during this period.

- Clonidine is another drug used to treat withdrawal symptoms after stopping opiate drugs such as heroin and morphine. It is undoubtedly effective in that context. But experience to date suggests that it is not particularly helpful in treating benzo-diazepine dependence. This a pity, because clonidine is non-addictive and, as it works by preventing many of the bio-chemical changes in the brain that lead to panic, it should be helpful in treating tranquilliser withdrawal.

Other drugs may help you to overcome tranquilliser dependence but they are not the whole answer. You may remember when you started tranquillisers you looked on them as a temporary crutch to help you through a difficult time. Unfortunately, in those who become dependent on tranquillisers it is as though the crutch becomes part of the body and cannot be discarded lightly.

If you are dependent on tranquillisers and only look for another tablet to help you out of your dependence you are very likely to repeat the cycle. You need to adopt the psychological strategies described in earlier pages to break the habit entirely.

7

If At First You Don't Succeed

Do not be tempted to read this chapter until you have honestly tried all the strategies described in previous chapters. The reasons why you should not do so will become clear later.

If you have indeed made a determined attempt to stop tranquillisers using at least several different methods you may approach this chapter in despair. You may blame yourself for failing to succeed using approaches that have worked for many others and you may even conclude that you are both weak-willed and spineless and that it is all your fault that you have failed to stop your tablets. This is the road to self-pity and you must change direction at once.

Reasons for failure

There are several explanations for your failure to break the tranquilliser habit and they do not involve blaming yourself. They include:

- A prolonged period of 'post-withdrawal blues'.
- Inability to achieve a period of relatively stress-free life during which to carry out your tranquilliser withdrawal.
- Insufficient cooperation from relatives and professionals in achieving your withdrawal programme.

There is another explanation also, but you should not seize it too readily. This is that you have a chronic anxiety state and will therefore need to take tranquillisers for many years, if not indefinitely. If this was true, you would be like Mrs Dempster on page 20. She, you will remember, has taken sleeping tablets for 28 years and has made it clear that she does not intend to stop them until the day she dies. Mrs Dempster is not an isolated case; many other people who have had very long term insomnia or anxiety cannot see any reason why they should not continue tranquillisers indefinitely.

Before you jump to the conclusion that you are like Mrs Dempster please ask yourself whether you really have had your anxious symptoms or persistent insomnia for as long as you can remember. We normally become aware of our mental functioning at about the age of nine or ten and for those people who become chronically tense and anxious the memories of these symptoms extend at least as far back as that age. Before deciding that you are chronically anxious stretch your memory a little and see if you can recall a tranquil time in your life.

Take the optimistic view that at some point you will be able to stop your tranquillisers. To test when the time is right make a small reduction in your dosage of tablets every six months or so. If you reduce from three tablets daily to two and a half and there is a marked increase in symptoms there is little point in continuing further. However, at some point you *will* find this reduction can be taken in your stride, and this will be the time to implement the withdrawal programme again.

Hopes and fears

A hope that many people cherish is the possibility of a new treatment being introduced for anxiety that could replace the existing tranquillisers. There is no harm in hoping, but it seems unlikely that the ideal tranquilliser – a drug that can produce calm with no side-effects or any degree of dependence – is ever going to be available.

Beware of any new tablet that is alleged to produce no dependence. This has been the boast of many tranquillisers introduced in the past but has always been followed by evidence that the original claim was mistaken. It often takes many years before the dependence risk of any substance is known. So, waiting for the next tablet to come along is rarely constructive.

If you are going to put off your withdrawal programme for months or even years you will need reassurance that you are not doing yourself harm in this way. It was pointed out in Chapter 1 that it is generally more difficult to stop taking tranquillisers the longer they have been taken. However, once you get beyond one year of continuous treatment there is little evidence that the degree of chemical dependence increases.

Psychological dependence may be greater, particularly if you have taken tablets for many years, but at least you can reassure yourself that you are not really adding to your addiction.

There has been some alarm recently about the possibility that the benzodiazepine tranquillisers produce brain abnormalities. Special computer scans of the brain have shown minor changes in some patients who have been taking benzodiazepines long term. However, these changes have not been found in all patients and some researchers have been unable to detect them. It is also far from clear whether these changes indicate any original abnormality in the brain, whether they are permanent or temporary changes or whether they could be due to other causes. For instance, much greater abnormalities are shown in people who have been drinking heavily for several months or years and may even occur after a short term bout of drinking. It is reassuring to know that many of these abnormalities disappear after a period of complete abstinence from alcohol.

The evidence that benzodiazepines produce brain abnormalities is, to use the Scottish expression, not proven. Research is continuing but in view of the conflicting evidence no conclusions can be drawn that will be helpful to people dependent on tranquillisers. From the evidence of similar but more serious abnormalities in patients with drinking problems it is reasonable to suppose that the abnormalities (if they exist) will disappear once you have stopped your drugs entirely. It would therefore be quite misleading to suggest that if you go on taking your tranquillisers for a little longer you will somehow 'rot your brain' with no hope of recovery.

It has also been alleged that cancer is caused by benzodiazepines but this is quite untrue. The only evidence that drugs such as diazepam could cause cancer came from one series of animal studies and has not been reproduced in any other investigations. Millions of people have been treated with benzodiazepines and there is no evidence that they are any more likely to get cancer than other individuals.

It is important, too, to get tranquilliser dependence into proportion. Perhaps it is worth reminding yourself of the dangers of addiction to substances other than tranquillisers.

- Heroin and other hard drugs given by injection lead to an addiction that dominates life: food and drink become less important than the next 'fix' and repeated injections without proper sterile precautions can lead to the transmission of diseases such as hepatitis and AIDS.
- Amphetamine addiction can lead to a severe psychosis like schizophrenia.
- Tobacco kills thousands of people anually through lung cancer and heart disease.
- Alcohol dependence leads to cirrhosis and liver failure.

By contrast, benzodiazepine dependence may produce unnecessary sedation, withdrawal symptoms after stopping treatment and questionable abnormalities in the brain of doubtful significance. Clearly then, the risks of taking benzodiazepines are in quite a minor league when compared with these other messengers of death.

I hope that you will thus be reassured that it is quite in order for you to put your withdrawal programme on ice, to be picked up again at some future date. Rather than try to force the pace and plan a time for withdrawal in advance, wait until you feel more settled and confident. Then make another reduction in your dosage and test the waters of withdrawal again.

If all goes well, start again on one of the programmes outlined earlier in this book. The lower your dose of tablets when you start the programme the more likely you are to have a successful outcome. If, for example, you were unable to make any progress last time, when taking 2 mg lorazepam daily do not assume the same problems will be repeated if you have managed to reduce gradually to 1 mg a day on a trial run before your formal withdrawal programme starts. You may have already broken the important barrier by reducing your daily dosage by half. From now on it could be plain sailing, particularly if you do not assume you are going to have problems in advance!

We all change, and your past failures in withdrawing from tranquillisers are not necessarily relevant for the future. You may choose to take drugs always but if you are determined to stop them the time will come when you can do this successfully, no matter how addicted you now appear to be. As we grow older we accept the troubles of life in a quieter and more reflective way and no longer get so agitated by trivial worries. We mellow, and mature. This leads to greater ability to cope with the uncertainties that cause anxiety and the unpleasantness of tranquilliser withdrawal. Instead of fighting the symptoms you 'ride' or ignore them, and although they do not just go away they become far more tolerable.

Remind yourself regularly of these words of encouragement. Or read them over again from time to time. Do not lose your determination to stop, and do not wait too long – though a gap of between six months and two years is reasonable. You will have learned some valuable lessons from your previous attempts to withdraw and you will at least know how not to proceed at your next attempt. You may even discover some unusual ways of coping with withdrawal symptoms:

- One of my patients found that when she stopped smoking soon after withdrawing from benzodiazepines her cravings for tobacco completely overcame all her withdrawal symptoms. As she was able to cope with the cravings she stayed off both her cigarettes and her benzodiazepines.
- Another patient decided to stop tranquillisers on the same day she started a job. She was so busy for the first few weeks that her withdrawal symptoms faded into the background and six weeks later she was amazed to realize they had disappeared altogether.

These examples illustrate that when tranquilliser dependence ceases to become the most important problem in your life it then becomes more manageable. The mountain of dependence seldom becomes a molehill but it need not remain an unconquered peak. You can bring it down to size, and most successful techniques will not only involve your becoming stronger and more determined but also succeed because they will reduce the significance of tranquilliser dependence in your life.

Above all, remember that dependence on tranquillisers is not a disease that will run its course no matter what you do. It is as much a state of mind as an illness and can be brought under control. Your break for freedom may be delayed but it will be just as sweet when it comes.

Appendix

Some people feel that they should be able to come off their tranquillisers without any outside assistance. If you are in this group you should not regard it as a sign of weakness to consult one of the organizations mentioned below. Others feel they cannot make the slightest reduction without some extra support. If you are in this second group, do make at least one determined attempt to stop your tranquillisers using one of the strategies described in this book, *before* consulting a help organization.

Self help groups

London area Jane Gerome, Tranx, c/o 2 St John's Road, Harrow, Middlesex, HA1 2EZ

Midlands Jane Bristow, Tranx Release, 106 Welstead Ave, Aspley, Nottingham (0602-760550)
Anita Gordon, Tranx Release, 14 Moorfield Sq, Southfields, Northamptonshire
Mike Morledge, Tranx Release, 18 Peveril Drive, Ilkeston, Derbyshire (0602-304287)

North East Shirley Trickett, SRN, PO Box 23, Heaton, Newcastle-Upon-Tyne, NE6 1LY

Ireland Tranx Release, P.O. Box 1378, Sheriff Street Dublin 1

There are increasing numbers of tranquilliser support groups being developed. It is likely that MIND will have knowledge of any newly organised groups in your area. To find out further details you can write to:

MIND, National Association for Mental Health, 22 Harley Street, London W1N 2ED or contact one of the six regional resource centres:

Northern MIND, 158 Durham Road, Gateshead, Tyne and Wear NE8 4EL

North West MIND, 21 Ribblesdale Place, Preston, Lancs PR1 3NA

Trent and Yorkshire MIND, First Floor Suite, White Buildings, Fitzallan Square, Sheffield, South Yorkshire S1 2AY

Wales MIND, 23 St Mary's Street, Cardiff CF1 2AA

West Midlands MIND, Princess Chambers (Third Floor), 52/54 Litchfield Street, Wolverhampton WV1 1DG

There has been a rapid expansion of self-help groups and other organizations for tranquilliser dependence and you should be able to find out the latest developments in your area by contacting your nearest Citizen's Advice Bureau.

In the United States and US territories there are drug abuse treatment agencies that deal with tranquilliser dependence as well as dependence on alcohol and other drugs.

There are also Veteran's Administration Hospital drug abuse treatment programmes in most states. Information about these, together with addresses and telephone numbers are listed in the National Directory of Drug Abuse Treatment Programmes which is obtainable from the National Clearinghouse for Drug Abuse Information P.O. Box 416, Kensington, Maryland MD 20795.

References

Mention is made several times in this book of the controversy surrounding tranquilliser dependence by medical authorities. Interested readers may wish to refer to the medical evidence before drawing their own conclusions. The list of references also includes some useful books on psychological treatments that may be used to overcome tranquilliser dependence.

Journals

Committee on the Review of Medicines (1980) *Systematic review of the benzodiazepines*. British Medical Journal, *1*, 910–912.

Covi, L., Lipman, R. S., Pattison, J. H., Derogatis, L. R. & Uhlenluth, E. H. (1973) *Length of treatment with anxiolytic sedatives and response to their sudden withdrawal.* Acta Psychiatrica Scandinavica, *49*, 51–64.

Fontaine, R., Chouinard, G. & Annable, L. (1984) *Rebound anxiety in anxious patients after abrupt withdrawal of benzodiazepine treatment.* American Journal of Psychiatry, *141*, 848–852.

Hallstrom, C. & Lader, M. H. (1981) *Benzodiazepine withdrawal phenomena.* International Pharmacopsychiatry, *16*, 235–244.

Kales, A., Soldatos, C. R., Bixler, E. O. & Kales, J. D. (1983) *Early morning insomnia with rapidly eliminated benzodiazepines.* Science, *220*, 95–97.

Lader, M. H., Ron, M. & Petursson, H. (1984) *Computed axial brain tomography in long-term benzodiazepine users.* Psychological Medicine, *14*, 203–206.

Maletzky, B. M. & Klotter, J. (1976) *Addiction to diazepam.* International Journal of Addiction, *11*, 95–115.

Murphy, S. M., Owen, R. T. & Tyrer, P. J. (1984) *Withdrawal symptoms after six weeks' treatment with diazepam.* Lancet, *ii*, 1389.

Owen, R. T. & Tyrer, P. J. (1983) *Benzodiazepine dependence: a review of the evidence.* Drugs, *25*, 385–398.

Petursson, H. & Lader, M. H. (1981) *Withdrawal from long-term benzodiazepine treatment.* British Medical Journal, *283*, 643–645.

Tyrer, P. (1980) *Dependence on benzodiazepines.* British Journal of Psychiatry, *137*, 576–577.

Tyrer, P., Rutherford, D. & Huggett, T. (1981) *Benzodiazepine withdrawal symptoms and propranolol.* Lancet, *i*, 520–522.

Tyrer, P. J., Owen, R. T. & Dawling, S. (1983) *Gradual withdrawal of diazepam after long-term therapy.* Lancet, *i*, 1402–1406.

Tyrer, P., Murphy, S., Oates, G. & Kingdon, D. (1985) *Psychological treatment for benzodiazepine dependence*. Lancet, i, 1042–1043.

Books

Vernon Coleman, *Life Without Tranquillisers* (Piatkus, 1985)

Barbara Gordon, *I'm Dancing as Fast as I can* (Harper & Row, New York, 1982)
   A personal account of someone hooked on tranquillisers.

Celia Haddon, *Women and Tranquillisers* (Sheldon Press, 1984)

Sandra Horn, *Relaxation: Modern Techniques for Stress Management* (Thorsons, 1986)

J. Marks, *Benzodiazepines: use, overuse, misuse, abuse* (MTP Press, 1978)

P. Snaith, *Clinical Neurosis* (Oxford University Press, 1981)

Claire Weekes, *Self-Help for Your Nerves* (Angus and Robertson, London, 1982)

Claire Weekes, *Peace from Nervous Suffering* (Angus and Robertson, London 1972)

Index